Introducing Astronomy

Elizabeth Swinbank and Barrie W. Jones

S194 Course Team

Barrie W. Jones	*Course Team Chair, Author*
Elizabeth Swinbank	*Author (S194 main text)*
Elizabeth Whitelegg	*Science Short Course Programme Director*
Isla McTaggart	*Course Manager*
Jenny Hudson	*Course Secretary*
Peter Twomey	*Editor*
Sue Dobson	*Graphic Design*
Sarah Hofton	*Graphic Design*
Jenny Nockles	*Graphic Design*
Lydia Eaton	*Library*
Tony W. Jones	*External Assessor*

The Open University, Walton Hall, Milton Keynes MK7 6AA

First published 2001

Written, edited, designed and typeset by the Open University.

Printed and bound in the United Kingdom by Thanet Press Limited, Margate, Kent.

ISBN 0 7492 3568 3

This text forms part of an Open University course, S194 *Introducing Astronomy*. Details of this and other Open University courses can be obtained from the Course Reservations and Sales Office, PO Box 724, The Open University, Milton Keynes MK7 6ZS, United Kingdom: tel. +44 (0) 1908 653231 or e-mail ces-gen@open.ac.uk.

For availability of this or other course components, contact Open University Worldwide Ltd, The Berrill Building, Walton Hall, Milton Keynes MK7 6AA, United Kingdom: tel. +44 (0) 1908 858585, fax +44 (0) 1908 858787, e-mail ouwenq@open.ac.uk. Alternatively, much useful course information can be obtained from the Open University's website http://www.open.ac.uk

1.2

s194i1.1

Contents

The Sun

Since ancient times, people have known the importance of the **Sun** in their daily lives. It provides light and warmth, and its regular motion across the sky gives rise to night and day. Not surprisingly, the Sun has been an object of worship in many cultures (Figure 1.1). We no longer think of the Sun as a powerful divine being, but it is still both loved and feared (Figure 1.2).

Figure 1.1 Mayan Sun temple.

Figure 1.2 Sunbathers bask in the Sun while risking exposure to its harmful ultraviolet rays.

For astronomers, the fascination of the Sun lies in the fact that it is our nearest **star**. By studying the Sun, we can gain some insight into the workings of the other millions of stars that can be seen in our night skies. Learning that the Sun is a star can come as a bit of a surprise. After all, the Sun is a huge, bright yellow glowing object — so bright that we can feel its warmth and it is dangerous to look at it directly. Stars, on the other hand, are mere silvery pinpoints of light that we can only see against the darkness of the night sky and certainly cannot feel. How can they possibly be the same sorts of things? The key lies in their distances.

In astronomical terms, the Sun is quite nearby, only about 150 million kilometres (93 million miles) from Earth. The stars we see at night are much further away; the nearest is about 40 *million million* kilometres from Earth, and most are much more distant. Imagine looking at a glowing light bulb first from very nearby and then moving it to a much greater distance. At first, you can see the shape of the bulb, but if you look from much further away, it looks like just a point of light.

1.1   Observing the Sun

Safety

Do not look directly at the Sun, either with your naked eyes or through glasses, binoculars or a telescope. To do so would risk permanently damaging your eyes.

1.1.1 The Sun at visible wavelengths

We are aware of the Sun as a bright yellow object in the sky. Normally, without using special instruments, we cannot study it in any more detail. However, a total eclipse of the Sun provides a rare opportunity to gain some insight into how the Sun works. This happens when the Moon passes in front of the Sun and exactly blocks out the bright light from the **photosphere** — the visible 'surface' of the Sun that gives out most of its light. In August 1999 a total eclipse was visible from parts of Europe, including part of Cornwall and Devon on the UK mainland. Unfortunately bad weather spoiled the view of totality from nearly everywhere in the UK, but people in some other parts of Europe were luckier. During the few minutes of totality (when the Moon completely obscures the bright photosphere), you can catch a glimpse of the Sun's **corona** — the tenuous (i.e. thin) outer parts of the Sun that stream outwards from its surface, emitting faint light. Figure 1.3 shows a photograph of the corona taken during a 1998 eclipse. Plates 1.1 and 1.2 in *IC* show views of the eclipsed Sun at two other eclipses.

Figure 1.3 The 1998 solar eclipse.

Study Note A table near the back of *IC* lists the dates of eclipses of the Sun and the Moon up to the year 2005, and indicates where they can be observed. In Chapter 3 of this book there is a map of solar eclipses up to 2020.

The image in Plate 1.2 shows another feature of the Sun not readily observable. This is its lower atmosphere, the chromosphere, just above the bright photosphere. As you can see from Plate 1.2, it has a pinkish colour. You can also see the so-called *prominences* — great glowing spurts of very hot material that shoot many thousands of kilometres from the Sun's surface. The corona, photosphere and prominences give a strong hint that the Sun is not simply glowing quietly. Rather, there are processes going on in the Sun that give rise to great upheavals and indicate an underlying power source. With temperatures of several million °C, the corona is extremely hot, much hotter than the photosphere which is 'only' about 5500 °C. And the corona streams out to several million kilometres above the Sun's surface, extending far beyond the main body of the Sun which is itself over a million kilometres across.

● Why are we not normally aware of the Sun's corona?

○ The bright light from the Sun's photosphere makes the sky blue, and so we cannot observe the much fainter light from the corona (rather as the light from a dim torch is unnoticeable on a bright sunny day).

Further hints of the Sun's nature can be seen in Plate 1.3. Sunspots are relatively dark patches on the photosphere, which last up to a few weeks and seem to be caused by strong magnetic fields that prevent hot material upwelling from the Sun's interior. In fact sunspots are still extremely hot and do give out light — they just appear dark in contrast to the even hotter and brighter surroundings.

1.1.2 Beyond visible light

During the twentieth century, astronomers extended their capabilities by developing telescopes that were sensitive not to normal visible light but to radio waves, X-rays, infrared, and ultraviolet. All these, along with visible light, are collectively called **electromagnetic radiation**, and all are given out by the Sun. The different types of electromagnetic radiation are all waves that travel through empty space at 300 000 kilometres per second — about 660 million miles per hour. Together these electromagnetic waves make up the so-called **electromagnetic spectrum**, which is a way of referring to the complete range of waves of this type.

At this point, you should read the Introduction to *IC* which gives some information about waves and electromagnetic radiation. Note the definition of the **wavelength** of radiation — the distance from one wave peak to the next. Notice too, the chart showing the wavelength range of the different types of electromagnetic radiation. The chart shows the wavelengths in metres, but only some of the marks are labelled. The marks go up in 'times ten' steps, so to the right of the 1 metre mark, the next mark shows a wavelength of 10 metres, then 100 m and finally 1000 m. Going to the left of the 1 metre mark, the next mark is 0.1 m, then 0.01 m (which is 1 cm), 0.001 m (1 mm) and so on. Going further to the left involves putting more and more zeros after the decimal point, so the wavelengths are sometimes measured in micrometres — millionths of a metre. 1 micrometre is 0.000 001 metres. (As you will see in Chapters 2 and 4, we can write very small and very large numbers in a different way which avoids writing strings of zeros.)

● Roughly what is the wavelength of visible light?

○ About 0.000 001 metres.

● What type of electromagnetic radiation has the longest wavelength? What, approximately, is its wavelength range?

○ Radio waves. On the chart, the shortest radio waves lie about one step to the left of the 1 m mark, which denotes a wavelength of 0.1 m. The band representing radio waves extends to the far right of the chart. The furthest mark on the right represent a wavelength of 1000 m (three steps to the right of the 1 m mark), so the chart shows that radio waves can have wavelengths of over a kilometre. (The radio waves used to broadcast BBC Radio 4 long-wave, for example, have a wavelength of 1500 m.)

1.1.3 The invisible Sun

We are aware of the Sun's infrared radiation because we feel its warmth.

○ How can we tell that it also gives out ultraviolet radiation?

○ We are aware that the Sun gives out ultraviolet radiation, since that is responsible for suntanning and sunburn.

The Sun's radio waves are weaker than its visible light but can readily be detected with even a small radiotelescope. Fortunately for our safety, the Earth's atmosphere shields us from the Sun's harmful X-rays, so these can only be studied using telescopes put into orbit above the atmosphere.

 By studying all its radiation, not just visible light, astronomers can get a more detailed view of the Sun. Plates 1.7, 1.8 and 1.9 in *IC* show how the Sun would appear if our eyes could see other types of radiation. For example, Plate 1.8 shows a large solar prominence — a huge cloud of gas rising from the Sun's surface. Prominences give out a lot of ultraviolet and visible radiation, and this picture was taken using ultraviolet-sensitive instruments for reasons that are explained in the caption. (A few captions contain terms that might not mean much to you, such as 'H-alpha' in the Plate 1.9 caption. It will not matter if you have to skip over such terms.)

 Note that the colours of images can be deceptive, since the colours have been added to bring out particular features, and different people choose to colour their pictures in different ways! For example, the X-ray view of the Sun (Plate 1.7a) uses white and yellow for the parts of the Sun which are giving out strong X-rays, and black for the fainter parts. Plate 1.7b, on the other hand, uses white to show where the Sun is giving out strong radio waves, but now red also indicates quite strong radiation, going down through yellow and green, with blue now being used to colour the parts that give out only faint radio waves. So comparing the colours of Plates 1.7a and b is meaningless; the important thing is to compare the regions they highlight. The radio waves seem to come mainly from around the Sun's equator, whereas the strong X-rays come from other parts, though it is important to realize that the images in Plate 1.7 were obtained on different dates, and so some of the transitory detail, such as sunspots, will differ from image to image. Nevertheless, by comparing and contrasting images such as these, astronomers can learn a great deal about the structure of the Sun and the sorts of processes that must be taking place both close to its surface and deep inside.

1.1.4 Updates

Since *IC* was produced, astronomers have continued to study the Sun in ever-increasing detail using both ground-based telescopes and space probes. If you have access to the internet, you can view some of the most recent solar observations on websites that can be accessed via the S194 ROUTES gateway:

The European SOHO and Ulysses space missions:

http://helio.estec.esa.nl/

The Japanese Yokhoh satellite plus other solar observations:

http://solar.physics.montana.edu/YPOP/index.html

The University of Hawaii Mees Solar Observatory:

http://www.solar.ifa.hawaii.edu/

1.2   Inside the Sun

We have hinted that the Sun must contain a power source in order to account for some of its observed features. In fact, the Sun's power source was a great puzzle in the nineteenth and early twentieth centuries. Fossil records and ideas about evolution were beginning to provide firm evidence that the Earth must be at least hundreds of millions of years old, rather than thousands of years as had been previously thought, and the Sun must be at least as old as the Earth. However, the Sun's fuel presented a problem. The only fuels known at the time were things such as coal, wood, oil, gas, and so on. It was fairly easy to calculate that, even if the Sun were made entirely of one of these fuels, and could get the necessary oxygen from its surroundings, it could only burn for a few thousand years at most while producing its current output of heat and light — not nearly long enough to sustain life on Earth over millions of years.

The problem of the Sun's fuel baffled many of the world's best scientists until nuclear reactions were discovered in the early twentieth century. This provided a totally new type of energy source. Rather than burning like coal or gas, nuclear reactions need no oxygen and produce vastly more heat and light for a given amount of fuel.

The British astronomer Arthur Eddington (1882–1944, Figure 1.4) calculated that, if the Sun were made mainly of hydrogen undergoing nuclear reactions, it could last for millions of years while producing a more-or-less steady heat and light output, and, what's more, its outward appearance would closely resemble that of the actual Sun. We now know that the hydrogen nuclear reactions will sustain the Sun for about ten thousand million years. (Nuclear reactions give so-called atomic bombs their great destructive power, and are harnessed more productively in the generation of electricity. The type of reactions that power the Sun, so-called fusion reactions involving hydrogen, are similar to those that take place in an H-bomb or hydrogen bomb but in the Sun they proceed steadily rather than as an explosion.)

Everything we know about nuclear reactions is based on experiments carried out in laboratories on Earth. It was Eddington's great triumph that he was able to take that knowledge and work out what would happen if nuclear reactions took place on a far greater scale than was possible on Earth, and to relate his deductions to what was known about the Sun. This example illustrates an important feature of astronomy — everything we know about the Universe beyond our own Earth and Moon (apart from a few planets that have been visited by space probes) must be deduced by observing from a very great distance. Astronomers have two main strands to their quest to understanding such distant objects. One strand involves the observations themselves, studying the appearance and movement of distant objects and measuring the light we receive from them. The other strand involves finding out how things behave on Earth and using that knowledge to interpret and account for the observations.

Using what they know about nuclear reactions and about how very hot materials behave, together with detailed observations of the Sun, scientists have pieced together a model (a mental picture) of what the Sun must be like deep inside. Such a picture is

Figure 1.4   Sir Arthur Eddington (1882–1944), astronomer and mathematician.

shown schematically in Plate 1.12 and described in the caption. The Sun does indeed consist largely of hydrogen, and it is fluid throughout. The nuclear reactions take place only in the Sun's **core** — that is, deep in its centre — because the hydrogen fuel needs to have a temperature of over 10 million °C, before its nuclear reactions can begin.

Activity 1.1 Describing the Sun (30 minutes)

Near the start of this chapter, we referred to the Sun as a 'huge, bright yellow glowing object'. From what you have read and studied so far, you now know rather more about the Sun than that simple description. Spend a few moments looking back through the text and the relevant pictures and captions from *IC*, and summarize what you have learned about the Sun's appearance and about its interior. Your summary should be in the form of a labelled sketch (maybe based on Plate 1.12). Try to make your summary as precise as possible — for example, include sizes and temperatures of the various parts of the Sun where you can. ◀

1.3 Measuring the Sun

In Sections 1.1 and 1.2 we referred to observations that can only be made using sophisticated telescopes, but in this section we turn to an observation you can carry out yourself. There are two reasons for this: one is to give you experience in carrying out a scientific measurement, and the other is to introduce some terminology used frequently in *IC* and many other astronomy books.

1.3.1 Angular size

Earlier, you looked at photographs taken during a total eclipse of the Sun, in which the Moon blocks out light from the Sun's photosphere enabling us to observe the chromosphere and corona. That this takes place is due to a remarkable coincidence. The Sun is very much bigger than the Moon — about 400 times bigger across its diameter — but it is also very much further away, by almost exactly the same amount. This means that the Sun and the Moon appear the same size in the sky. We can describe this by saying that the Sun and Moon have the same **angular size**, as illustrated by the lower diagram on the third page of the introduction in *IC*. Figure 1.5 shows what angular size is. Imagine lines drawn from your eye to the extreme edges of an object you are observing. The angle between the lines gives the object's angular size. Angular size thus depends on an object's actual size and its distance from the eye of the observer.

You are probably used to angles measured in degrees (360° for a full circle, 90° for a right angle, and so on). However, although the objects studied by astronomers are very large, they are at such vast distances that their angular sizes are very small.

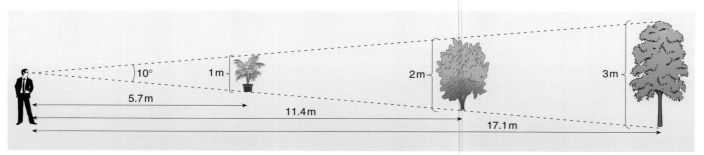

Figure 1.5 Objects with an angular size of 10°.

These angles could be written as fractions or as decimal numbers, but in practice it is more usual to use subdivisions of degrees. A degree can be divided into 60 minutes (minutes of arc, or arcmin, to distinguish them from minutes of time), and a minute of arc is further divided into 60 seconds of arc, or arcsec. A single tick is used to represent arcmin, so 1/60 of a degree is written 1′. A double tick denotes arcsec, so 1/3600 of a degree (1/60 of an arcmin) is written 1″.

Angular size is a very useful measurement in astronomy, since angular sizes are *very* much easier to measure than actual sizes as they refer simply to how large an object appears in the sky. The Sun and Moon both have an angular size of about half a degree.

● What angle is this?

○ This is the angle between two imaginary lines drawn from our eye to the extremities of the disc of the Moon.

If you flick through *IC*, you will notice that most of the pictures have a scale. In some cases, such as pictures of the Sun and planets, the scale gives the actual size in kilometres, but when you get to Part 3, which is about very distant objects, the scales give the angular sizes in degrees, arcmin or arcsec.

1.3.2 Angular size, actual size and distance

The angular size of an object is determined uniquely by its actual size and its distance. From the upper diagram on the third page of the introduction in *IC* you can see that the larger the distance the *smaller* the angular size. You can also appreciate that the larger the actual size of the object the *larger* its angular size. The expression

angular size = (actual size ÷ distance)

has these properties and in fact it gives us an excellent approximation for objects with small angular sizes, such as astronomical objects. This expression gives angular size in units that are probably unfamiliar to you. The unit is the radian, but we will not be using these in this course. To get the angular size in degrees please accept that we have to modify the expression slightly to

angular size in degrees = 57 × (actual size ÷ distance)

Try this expression on Figure 1.5.

● Calculate 57 × (actual size ÷ distance) for each of the plants in Figure 1.5.

○ The values are 57 × (1 m ÷ 5.7 m), 57 × (2 m ÷ 11.4 m), 57 × (3 m ÷ 17.1 m), which is 10° in each case (as expected).

To do Activity 1.2, you need to know that the Moon's diameter is 3476 km. You may wonder how this can be measured from the Earth. In principle it is a surprisingly easy measurement to make. First, you have to find the diameter of the Earth, which can be worked out by measuring how much its surface curves; you may be surprised to learn that this measurement was made in about 235 BC by the Greek astronomer Eratosthenes, and that his value was quite close to our modern measurement of 12 756 km (for the equatorial diameter — the Earth is slightly flattened). The sizes of Earth and Moon can be compared by looking at the Earth's shadow on the Moon's surface during a partial eclipse of the Moon (Figure 1.6) — careful measurement reveals that the Earth's diameter is 3.67 times that of the Moon.

Figure 1.6 A partial eclipse of the Moon.

Activity 1.2   The distance to the Moon (30 minutes)

This activity needs to be done when the Moon is clearly visible in the sky. (It need not be done at night, and in fact can be easier in daytime or twilight.) DO NOT ATTEMPT THIS ACTIVITY ON THE SUN.

For the activity you will need the following items:

- selection of coins (e.g. 1p, 5p, 10p)
- straight rod (e.g. piece of dowelling or garden cane) at least 2 m long
- tape measure at least 2 m long
- ruler marked in centimetres and millimetres
- Blu-Tack or Plasticine
- pocket calculator.

Set up an arrangement with a coin fixed to a rod in such a way that the coin just 'eclipses' the Moon. Figure 1.7 shows one possible set-up.

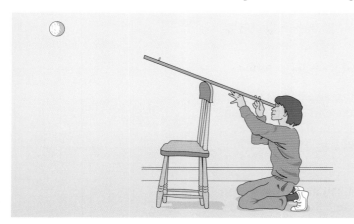

Figure 1.7   One possible arrangement for eclipsing the Moon.

First try different coins to get one that is the right size to eclipse the Moon when fixed somewhere on the rod. Then adjust the position of the coin until it *just* blocks your view of the Moon. In practice this is less easy than it sounds, as there will always be some haze visible around the edge of the coin — try to get the best match.

Measure the distance from the coin to the end of the rod where you have placed your eye, and measure the coin's diameter. Record your values here.

diameter of coin = ………… mm

distance of coin = ………… mm

You now have the measurements that will enable you to calculate the angular size of a coin that has the same angular size as the Moon.

First, use your two measurements on the coin to calculate its angular size in degrees, using the formula introduced earlier, adapted to the current case, i.e.

angular size of coin in degrees = 57 × (diameter of coin ÷ distance of coin)

= ………….

Your answer should be about half a degree (0.5°). Any value between 0.4° and 0.6° is OK. This is also your measurement of the angular size of the Moon. So, write down

angular size of Moon in degrees = ………

The next step is to calculate the *distance* to the Moon. Just as for the coin

angular size of Moon in degrees = 57 × (diameter of Moon ÷ distance of Moon).

This expression can be rearranged to give

distance of Moon = 57 × (diameter of Moon ÷ angular size of Moon in degrees).

(Take this on trust if you cannot see it.) Now calculate the distance to the Moon, using your value for its angular size and 3476 km for its diameter.

distance of Moon = 57 × ………… km.

You might like to compare your result with the accurately-measured value of the Moon's distance: 384 500 km. You will not have got exactly this value, but you probably got something around 300 000 to 500 000 km, which is pretty good for a quick and fairly rough measurement. ◄

The same technique as in Activity 1.2 can also be used to work out the Sun's distance if you know its size. *But under no circumstances should you try Activity 1.2 with the Sun, since that would seriously endanger your eyes.*

1.4   Chapter summary

The essential points of Chapter 1 are as follows.

1   The Sun is a star, giving out all types of electromagnetic radiation.

2   Electromagnetic radiation consists of waves which can travel through empty space and which cover a huge range of wavelengths.

3   The Sun is powered by nuclear reactions in its core which enable it to produce electromagnetic radiation steadily over thousands of millions of years.

4   The Sun and Moon have approximately the same angular size when viewed from the Earth.

5   The angular size of an object depends on its actual size and its distance from an observer.

1.5   End-of-chapter questions

Question 1.1   According to the chart in the introduction to *IC*, what is the approximate wavelength range (in metres) of microwaves? ◄

Question 1.2   Plates 1.7, 1.8 and 1.9 show images of the Sun obtained using various types of electromagnetic radiation. By studying the captions and referring to the chart in the introduction to *IC*, list these pictures in order of the wavelength of radiation used, starting with the shortest. (Note that H-alpha is a visible wavelength.) ◄

Question 1.3   In a sentence or two, explain why the problem of the Sun's fuel puzzled scientists, and say how the discovery of nuclear reactions solved the puzzle. ◄

Question 1.4   The Sun is about 150 million km from the Earth. Use information from Section 1.3 about the angular diameters of the Sun and Moon to calculate the Sun's approximate diameter. You will need to note that

actual size = (angular size in degrees × distance) ÷ 57.

(Do not spend more than a few minutes trying to show that this is so. There is a second way to tackle this question — see if you can find it.) ◄

Question 1.5   A large sunspot is observed to have an angular size one-twentieth that of the Sun. Taking the Sun's angular size to be 0.5°, what is the angular size of the sunspot? Express your answer in (a) arcmin (b) arcsec. ◄

2 The Planets

In this chapter, we stay in the neighbourhood of the Earth and Sun and explore some of the other objects that make up the **Solar System** — that is, the **Sun** and the objects associated with it, including the **planets**.

2.1 The Solar System

An overview of our current knowledge of the Solar System is given in the introduction to Part 2 of *IC*. The first two paragraphs are particularly relevant — you should read them *now* and study the layout and scale of the Solar System on the page that faces this text. The text goes on to discuss how we think the Solar System was formed from a cloud known as the 'solar nebula', and outlines some of the processes that take place within planets; you will be prompted to read these parts later in this chapter.

There are several things to notice about the diagram in Part 2 of *IC* that shows the layout and scale of the Solar System. First, it is drawn as an oblique view, so the orbits of planets appear highly elongated. Viewed 'from above' they are almost circular. Even Mercury's orbit, which is one of the least circular, looks pretty much like a circle at a casual glance, as you can see from Figure 2.1.

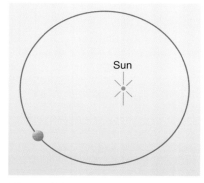

Figure 2.1 An accurate scale drawing of Mercury's orbit.

Another thing to notice is the scales of the two parts of the diagram. The upper part, showing the orbits, covers distances of thousands of millions of kilometres, whereas the lower part shows that even Jupiter, the largest planet, has a diameter of only 143 000 kilometres. Activity 2.1 shows the difficulties associated with making a scale model of the Solar System, and also illustrates the vast distances between the planets compared to their sizes. In practice you might not be able to complete the activity, but even just thinking about it is instructive!

Activity 2.1 Modelling the Solar System (30 minutes)

To illustrate the relative sizes of the planets, collect the items of fruit listed in Table 2.1 which represent the planets on a scale of 1 cm to 5000 km. Alternatively, cut circles of paper to represent the planets on this scale.

On this scale, a model Sun would have a diameter of about 2 m. Draw a circle of this size using a piece of string 1 m long, fixed at one end.

When you have assembled these objects you can get a feel for the relative sizes of the major bodies in the Solar System. Note that a grapefruit (Uranus) is about ten times the diameter of a cherry (Mercury), but the volume ratio is much larger — you could fit about 1000 cherries into the volume occupied by a grapefruit.

Now look at Table 2.2, which shows the distances to the planets on the same scale. Arrange (some of) your pieces of fruit at these distances from your 'Sun'.

As an alternative, make a smaller scale model showing the distances between the planets. Take a piece of string 6 m long, and mark the distances to the planets using a scale of 1 cm to 10 million km (tie knots in the string at appropriate places, or tie on labels representing the planets, or mark the string with felt-tipped pen). You cannot show the actual planets to scale on this model. ◀

Table 2.1 Modelling the sizes of the planets on a scale of 1 cm to 5000 km.

Planet	Approx. diameter	Represented by...	Approx. model diameter
Mercury	5000 km	cherry	1.0 cm
Venus	12 000 km	plum	2.4 cm
Earth	13 000 km	plum	2.6 cm
Mars	7000 km	cherry	1.4 cm
Jupiter	140 000 km	water melon	28 cm
Saturn	120 000 km	pumpkin	24 cm
Uranus	51 000 km	grapefruit	10 cm
Neptune	48 000 km	orange	9.6 cm
Pluto	2400 km	pea	0.5 cm

Table 2.2 Modelling the distances of the planets on a scale of 1 cm to 5000 km.

Planet	Approx. distance from Sun	Approx. model distance
Mercury	58 million km	116 m
Venus	108 million km	216 m
Earth	150 million km	300 m
Mars	228 million km	456 m
Jupiter	778 million km	1.6 km
Saturn	1430 million km	2.9 km
Uranus	2870 million km	5.7 km
Neptune	4500 million km	9.0 km
Pluto	5900 million km	12 km

Study Note   A table near the back of *IC* ('Basic data on the planets') lists more precise values for the sizes and distances of the planets, along with much other information.

2.1.1   Scale sizes and large numbers

The figures in Tables 2.1 and 2.2 are for a model on a scale of 1 cm to 5000 km. How much bigger is the real Solar System than the model?

One metre is one hundred centimetres, and one kilometre is a thousand metres, so there are one hundred thousand centimetres in a kilometre. (That is, 1 km = 100 000 cm). In five thousand kilometres there are five hundred thousand thousand centimetres — in other words five hundred million centimetres, so the actual Solar System is five hundred million (500 000 000) times bigger than the model.

As you have seen above and in Activity 2.1, writing the sizes and distances of the Moon and planets involves very large numbers. Rather than writing out large numbers in words, or writing strings of zeros, we can adopt a shorthand sometimes known as **scientific notation**. Table 2.3 shows how it works. For example, 100 is 10×10, which can also be written as 10^2 and read as 'ten to the power of 2'.

1000 is $10 \times 10 \times 10$, or 10^3, and so on. In this notation, we can write five thousand as 5×10^3 (5 times one thousand), and five hundred million becomes 5×10^8, which is much more compact, and also easier to read than 500 000 000 (once you get used to it) — you don't have to count the zeros because the 'power' (the small number) tells you how many there are.

Table 2.3 Powers of ten.

100 =	$10 \times 10 =$	10^2
1000 =	$10 \times 10 \times 10 =$	10^3
10 000 =	$10 \times 10 \times 10 \times 10 =$	10^4
100 000 =	$10 \times 10 \times 10 \times 10 \times 10 =$	10^5
1000 000 =	$10 \times 10 \times 10 \times 10 \times 10 \times 10 =$	10^6

and so on…

In scientific notation, Mercury's diameter in kilometres could be written as 5×10^3 km, or in metres as 5×10^6 m (5000 000 m). The Earth's diameter would be written as 1.3×10^4 km or 1.3×10^7 m ($1.3 \times 10 000 000$ m). The convention is to write just one number before the decimal point — writing 13×10^6 m would not be incorrect, just unconventional.

◐ The distance around the Earth's equator is about 4×10^7 m. Write this value using ordinary notation.

○ 10^7 is 10 000 000 (seven zeros). So 4×10^7 m is the same as 40 000 000 m.

● Write the distance round the Earth's equator measured in kilometres. Use both ordinary and scientific notation.

◑ 40 000 000 m is 40 000 km, which can also be written as 4×10^4 km.

● Using scientific notation, write the diameters of Mars and Saturn in metres.

○ From Table 2.1, Mars has a diameter 7000 km i.e. 7000 000 m, which is 7×10^6 m. Saturn's diameter is 120 000 km i.e. 120 000 000 m which is 1.2×10^8 m.

We will return to scientific notation in later chapters — it is widely used not only in astronomy but in many other areas of science.

2.2 The planets

The individual planets themselves have fascinated human beings for centuries. Unlike the stars, which appear in fixed patterns night after night (as we will discuss in Chapter 3), the planets move across these patterns. Their movement, and the Earth's movement about the Sun, mean that we see them in different directions depending on where they are and where we are. Once it was established (in the fifteenth and sixteenth centuries) that the Earth and other planets all orbit the Sun, and the development of telescopes gave astronomers a more detailed view, people began to wonder about life on other planets. In the nineteenth century, markings on the surface of Mars were interpreted as channels, or even as canals (see Figure 2.2), and it was thought by some scientists that Mars was inhabited by intelligent beings.

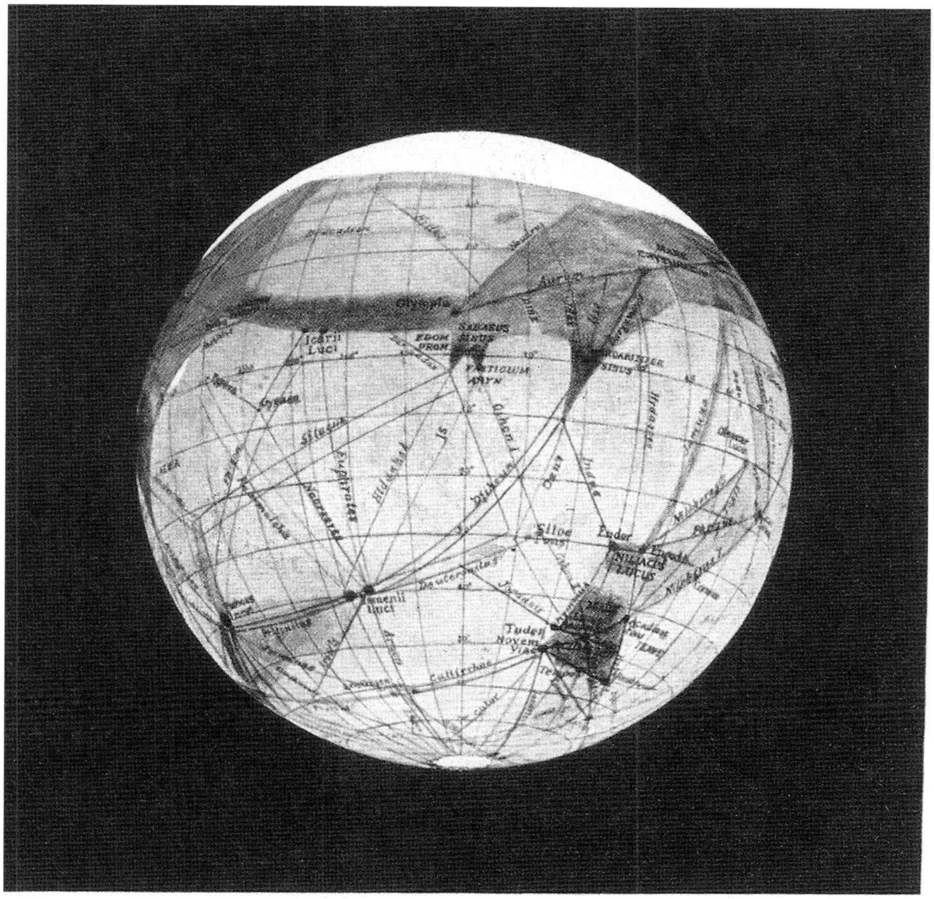

Figure 2.2 A drawing of the supposed channels, or 'canals', on the surface of Mars, drawn in 1905 by the American astronomer Percival Lowell.

APPEARANCE OF MARS IN 1905

As telescopes improved, and space probes were developed and visited Mars, it became clear that the 'canals' did not exist; a few were misinterpretations of splodges and streaks, but most have no discernible counterparts on the martian surface. There was no evidence for any life-forms at all. But the fascination with the planets as 'other worlds' continues and, while canal-building Martians are now known not to exist, there is still a possibility that very simple living organisms, such as bacteria, may be present on other planets. Telescopes also reveal that, just as the Earth has its Moon, some of the other planets also have smaller objects orbiting around them. Collectively these 'moons' are known as **satellites** — a term that has become associated with artificial objects but which also refers to natural objects.

Our current knowledge of the planets and their satellites is based on what astronomers can observe using telescopes, and on information collected by space probes. Many of these have produced spectacular images, some of which are included in *IC*. Together with knowledge gained from studying our own planet Earth, such observations provide us with an understanding of conditions on other planets, and also give some clues as to how the Solar System might have formed.

Even just a quick browse through Part 2 of *IC* reveals the rich variety of the planets and their satellites. Those images are arranged in a particular order so as to tell a story, but it is perhaps easier to start by looking at Mercury (the planet nearest the Sun, Figure 2.3) and work outwards to Pluto (Figure 2.4) as indicated in Table 2.4.

Figure 2.3 The planet Mercury. Its surface is heavily cratered. (The horizontal lines are artefacts of the imaging process.)

Figure 2.4 Hubble Space Telescope image of Pluto and its satellite, Charon. Pluto is so distant that it has not yet been imaged in detail by an Earth-based telescope, and no space probe has yet flown close to it.

One way in which astronomers (and scientists in general) try to make sense of what they observe is to look for patterns and similarities. Astronomers have looked for ways in which planets resemble one another in order to be able to talk about groups of planets rather than individuals, and this has helped throw some light on their history. Activity 2.2 is concerned with this classification process.

Table 2.4 Images of planets in order of distance from the Sun.

Planet	Global view(s)	Close-up view(s)
Mercury	Figure 2.3 (this book)	Plate 2.4
Venus	Plates 2.17 & 2.29	Plates 2.18–2.20
Earth	Plate 2.30	Plates 2.24 & 2.25
Mars	Plate 2.12	Plates 2.13–2.16, 2.31, 2.32
Jupiter	Plates 2.34 & 2.35 (part)	Plate 2.40
Saturn	Plates 2.34 & 2.35 (part)	Plates 2.41, 2.42 & 2.51
Uranus	Plates 2.8 (background), 2.34 (part) & 2.37	—
Neptune	Plates 2.34 (part) & 2.38	Plate 2.39
Pluto	Figure 2.4 (this book)	—

Activity 2.2   Classifying planets (20 minutes)

Study the images listed in Table 2.4 and their captions. Near the back of *IC*, the table 'Basic data on the planets' lists the sizes, and the numbers of rings and satellites of each planet (you can ignore the rest of the table).

Suggest ways in which planets might be classified on the basis of this information. What characteristics do you think would lead to a helpful classification system? Size? Colour? Presence of rings? Number of natural satellites? Some other characteristic? For each characteristic, try to think of reasons why it might, or might not, be a sensible way to classify the planets. ◀

Several of the characteristics suggested in Activity 2.2 (size, satellites and rings) lead to the same way of grouping the planets. Astronomers generally classify the planets into two main groups. The **terrestrial** (Earth-like) **planets** — Mercury, Venus, Earth and Mars — lie closest to the Sun, are all of fairly similar size, and have few or no natural satellites (two at most) and no rings. The **giant planets** — Jupiter, Saturn, Uranus and Neptune — are very much larger than the terrestrial planets, and lie much further from the Sun. Their orbits are also much more widely spaced than those of the terrestrial planets, as you will have seen from Activity 2.1 and Table 2.2. The giant planets all have several satellites and some rings — Saturn's being by far the most prominent. Pluto is the odd one out. It lies not very far beyond Neptune, but is as small as a terrestrial planet. Its great distance makes it difficult to study, but some astronomers believe that it is not a true planet at all and its oddness suggests that it may have a different origin from the rest.

The broad similarities within the two main groups of planets do not just relate to their appearance. The terrestrial planets are all made from rocky materials. Rocky materials can be liquid or solid, depending on the temperature, but inside the terrestrial planets they are solid in most regions. Jupiter and Saturn are made largely of hydrogen and helium. We can see this directly in their atmospheres, but knowledge of how materials behave, deduced in Earth-based laboratories, leads astronomers to conclude that the atmospheres of these two planets become gradually thicker with depth. These atmospheres become liquid deep in their interiors with perhaps a core at the centre consisting largely of water and rocky materials, which are liquid at the high temperatures found there.

Uranus and Neptune can be thought of as resembling Jupiter and Saturn, but with less massive envelopes of hydrogen and helium, and so they contain a substantially higher proportion of water and rocky materials.

The introduction to Part 2 of *IC* includes 'A note on planetary interiors', and this would be a good time to read it.

○ Two sorts of materials that make up planets can be broadly classified as either **icy materials** or **rocky materials**. Suggest definitions of these two terms.

○ Rocky materials are those that are solid at temperatures typical of the Earth's surface, and include rocks (!), soil and metals. Rocky materials melt at high temperatures, such as occur naturally deep inside planets or are created artificially in furnaces. Icy materials are those that are normally liquid or gas, or else melt very easily, at the Earth's surface. Icy materials include water (in the form of ice, liquid water or water vapour), ammonia and methane. At sufficiently low temperatures (such as those found at the surfaces of planets lying far from the Sun), icy materials are solid.

Theories of how the Solar System formed can account for the differences in composition between the various planets — broadly speaking, the controlling factor is distance from the Sun. The terrestrial planets formed close to the Sun, where the temperatures were (and still are) much higher than where the giants formed, and so water could not be acquired by these planets as they formed, and therefore the terrestrial planets never got massive enough to capture hydrogen and helium. Plate 2.1 shows an artist's impression of the Solar System very early in its history, and the caption outlines some of our ideas about how the planets are thought to have formed. Further ideas are given in the third paragraph of the introduction to Part 2 of *IC*, which you should also read now.

Activity 2.3   Planet formation (20 minutes)

Outline how the Solar System's planets are believed to have formed, and how this can account for the different compositions of the giant and terrestrial planets. ◀

2.3 Orbits

The Solar System is made up, broadly speaking, of objects orbiting other objects in more-or-less circular paths. The planets orbit the Sun and they in their turn have satellites and rings in orbit around them. The orbits of objects in the Solar System follow a well-ordered pattern as described in the introduction to Part 2 of *IC*.

⚫ Why can the orbits of Solar System objects be described as well-ordered?

⚪ The orbits of the planets and asteroids all lie in (almost) the same plane, and they all move around the Sun in the same direction.

Most planets rotate on their axes in this same direction. The orbits of planetary satellites lie close to the equators of their 'parent' planets, and most satellites travel in the same direction as their planet's rotation. (As you will see later, this well-ordered motion helps us to explain the origin of the orbital motion of planets and their satellites.)

An understanding of orbital motion is fundamental to astronomy. It is crucial in the design of space missions to the Moon and other planets and, as you will see later (in Chapter 6), it enables astronomers to deduce the existence of planets associated with other stars. Stars themselves can be found in orbit around one another, and stars also move in orbit about the centre of a galaxy. In this section we introduce some key ideas about orbital motion.

People sometimes wonder what keeps the Moon in orbit and stops it crashing to the Earth. This is a perfectly reasonable thing to ask. If you lift an object above the Earth's surface and let it go, it falls to the ground, pulled by the force of gravity. Why should the same not happen to the Moon? Indeed, why do the Earth and other planets not fall into the Sun? To answer that question, and to see what role gravity plays in the story, we need first to examine circular motion.

2.3.1 Circular motion

As you can demonstrate for yourself in Activity 2.4, if you set an object in motion it will move in a straight line unless there is something pushing or pulling it into a curved path. To keep something moving in a circular path, it needs constantly to be nudged sideways — there needs to be some force (that is, a push or pull) directed towards the centre of the circle. The technical name for a force directed towards the centre of a circle is a **centripetal force** (centripetal means 'centre-seeking').

Activity 2.4 Motion in a circle (20 minutes)

For this activity you will need a ping-pong ball or large marble (or similar smooth smallish ball), a smooth table-top or floor, and about 1 m of string (or wool) attached to a cork or a lump of Plasticene (or other object of similar size and weight than can easily be fixed to your string). The second part of the activity (whirling the cork) needs to be done somewhere well away from people or objects that might be hit by a flying cork — ideally do it out of doors; do *not* use a heavy object in this part of the activity.

First roll the ping-pong ball (without spinning it) along the smooth surface. Notice that it moves in a straight line.

Next try to get it to follow a curved path (again, without spinning it). You will find that, left to itself, it always follows a straight line. To get a curved path, you need to

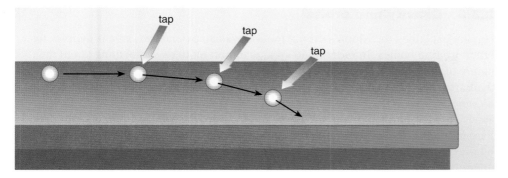

Figure 2.5   Making a ping-pong ball travel in a curve.

keep nudging it sideways as shown in Figure 2.5. If you could exert a steady force rather than a series of taps, you would be able to get the ball moving in a smooth curve because you were supplying the necessary centripetal force.

One way to supply a steady centripetal force is to pull on a piece of string attached to the moving object. Try whirling your cork or Plasticene in a horizontal circle — you can feel that you need to keep pulling on the string as you do so.

Finally, let go of the string while whirling the cork and notice the way it moves. You should be able to see that it continues to move in the way it was heading at the time, as shown in Figure 2.6. ◄

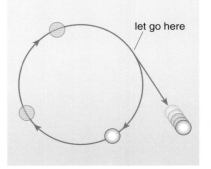

Figure 2.6   Letting go of a whirling cork.

The need for a centripetal force applies to *all* cases of circular motion. In the example of the whirling cork, the force providing the inward pull is easy to see, but sometimes it is less so. For example, when a car is rounding a bend, the thrust of the engine and the grip of the tyres on the road combine to produce the necessary centripetal force.

2.3.2   The Moon's orbital motion

What about the Moon? The Moon orbits the Earth in a (near) circular orbit.

● What must be providing the centripetal force for the Moon's orbit?

○ The force of gravity acting between the Earth and the Moon keeps the Moon moving in its near-circular path.

● What would happen to the Moon if gravity suddenly stopped acting?

○ The Moon would drift off into space since there would be nothing to hold it in orbit around the Earth.

If the Moon were simply to be suspended above the Earth and dropped, rather than moving in orbit, it would indeed move directly towards us pulled by gravity. In fact, it also has 'sideways' motion, and the overall effect is an orbit around the Earth. So, in wondering why the Moon does *not* fall towards the Earth, we should perhaps ask what gave it its sideways motion. It is thought that the Moon formed from material ejected from the Earth in a giant impact (see the caption to Plate 2.2). Some of this material would have ended up swirling around the Earth, where it gathered to form the Moon. The swirling motion is preserved in the form of orbital motion of the Moon.

So, in summary, we can explain the Moon's orbital motion. It acquired its motion from the swirling material from which it formed, and is kept in a near-circular orbit by the force of gravity acting between it and the Earth.

2.3.3   Gravity and orbits

Having explained the Moon's orbital motion we can extend the same principles to other orbiting bodies. In order to do so, it is important to say something about the nature of gravity. We are familiar with gravity as the force that pulls objects towards the Earth, but Earth is not special in exerting this force. In fact gravity acts between *all* objects. Just as the Earth and Moon are attracted towards one another by gravity, so also are the Earth and you, the Earth and the Sun, the Sun and Jupiter, Jupiter and its satellite Europa — and so on. Even you and this book are attracted to one another by gravity, but the force between small objects is so weak that it normally goes unnoticed and we are normally only aware of gravity when at least one of the objects is getting on for planet-sized.

● Neptune moves in a near-circular orbit around the Sun. What provides the necessary centripetal force?

○ The Sun and Neptune attract one another by the force of gravity, and this prevents Neptune from drifting off into space away from the Solar System.

The other satellites, and the planets themselves, were all born from material that was already in a swirling orbital motion, and so the satellites and planets to which such material gave birth also had initial orbital motion, sustained ever since by gravity.

The principles used to explain orbital motion of natural objects apply equally to artificial ones such as satellites placed in orbit, or space probes circling other planets. Nowadays there are many artificial satellites above the Earth. Why do they not fall down? This is really the same as the Moon question we raised earlier. If satellites were just placed above the Earth, they would indeed fall down. Rather, they are launched 'sideways' from a spacecraft, and gravity pulls them into a circular path around the Earth. The idea of doing this goes back a surprisingly long way. When Isaac Newton (1642–1727) was studying the motion of the Moon and falling bodies he suggested that a shell fired from a mountain-top cannon at sufficiently high speed would go into orbit as shown in Figure 2.7. In Newton's time this could only be a 'thought experiment', and it was some time before technology made this possible.

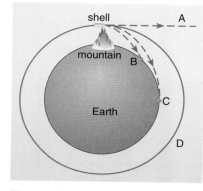

Figure 2.7   Launching a satellite into orbit. The launch speeds increase in the order B, C, D, A.

2.4   Exploring the planets

Since the middle of the twentieth century, the development of space probes has led to a tremendous explosion in our knowledge of the planets. Space missions can provide close-up views of planets and their satellites, and spectacular images from two recent missions can be seen at:

The Mars Global Surveyor

http://mars.jpl.nasa.gov/mgs/

The Galileo Orbiter for Jupiter and its satellites:

http://www.jpl.nasa.gov/galileo/

Space probes can also land on planetary surfaces and carry out experiments, sending the results back via radio communications. The TV programme 'Design for an alien world' (found on the video) tells the story of one such mission — the joint European–American Cassini–Huygens mission to Saturn and its satellite Titan. This would be a good time to view the TV programme, which also relates to Activity 2.5. Its running time is 30 minutes.

The TV programme focuses on the design of some of the instruments on the Huygens probe, destined to land on Titan's surface. When the Cassini mission reaches Saturn in 2004, the Huygens probe will be released and will descend through Titan's atmosphere. When the group started work in 1989, very little was known about Titan's surface, so the probe had to be designed to cope with a variety of possible conditions. The long timescale of the project, the international collaboration, the educated guesswork and the careful testing are all typical of missions to explore other planets. After watching the programme, you may notice some similarities — and also some contrasts — with other space missions that feature in the news from time to time.

Activity 2.5   Design for an alien world (30 minutes)

Watch the TV programme 'Design for an alien world'. As you do so, bear the following questions in mind:

- How many years were taken to plan the project, and to build and test the instruments?
- How long will it take for the Cassini spacecraft to reach Saturn?
- How many different institutions and nations are involved in the project?
- What tests are carried out before the instruments are despatched into space?
- How did data from the Hubble telescope help with the Cassini mission? ◄

At the time of writing (Autumn 2000) the Cassini mission still had some way to travel before reaching its destination. If you have access to the internet, you can find out the most recent news of Cassini from websites that can be accessed via the S194 ROUTES gateway:

The UK Cassini–Huygens home page:

> http://www.ssd.rl.ac/news/cassini/

The NASA Cassini–Huygens home page:

> http://jpl.nasa.gov/cassini

As you will have seen in the TV programme, astronomers already knew that Titan had a nitrogen-based atmosphere before launching the Cassini mission. But the reason for the presence of methane was not clear, and they thought that there might be some processes on Titan's surface that release methane into the atmosphere. This puzzle illustrates some important aspects of planetary science. One is that planetary scientists — like all astronomers — strive to account for their observations in terms of what they already know and understand (e.g. from experiments on Earth). Another is that *processes* are important on and within planets and satellites — these are illustrated in Activity 2.6, which gives just a brief glimpse of the richness of planetary science as a field of study.

Activity 2.6   Shaping the surface (20 minutes)

Many of the pictures in *IC* illustrate processes that shape the solid surfaces of planets and satellites. Look through Part 2 of *IC* to find at least one picture that illustrates each of the following:

- Craters produced by impacts (of small bodies from space)
- Mountains produced by volcanoes
- Regions shaped by lava flows (icy or rocky lavas)
- Channels or canyons produced or modified by water. ◄

There is another process that is particularly important in shaping the Earth's surface, though it is not explicitly mentioned in the captions in *IC*. The motion of large 'plates' that make up the surface has created the continents and ocean basins, and many other features too, such as most of the mountain ranges on the Earth (for example the Alps, the Himalaya and the Andes).

2.5 Meteors, meteorites, asteroids and comets

Extraterrestrial fragments of material entering the Earth's atmosphere are sometimes observed as 'shooting stars' as they heat up on passing through the atmosphere — more precisely, they are called **meteors**. If any remnant survives passage through the atmosphere and reaches the Earth's surface it is called a **meteorite**. Plates 2.46 and 2.47 and their captions give some more details about these fascinating 'visitors from space'. Some of them are rocks left over from the formation of the Solar System, some are pieces of **asteroids** (small bodies mainly found between Mars and Jupiter — see the diagram in the introduction to Part 2 of *IC*), but a few are fragments chipped off the surface of the Moon or Mars (where the low gravity and tenuous atmospheres enable them to escape). Detailed analysis of meteorites can therefore give information about conditions in the early Solar System, or about the Moon or Mars. Plate 2.50 shows a meteorite whose composition suggests it comes from Mars. In 1996, another martian meteorite known as ALH84001 caused great excitement. Microscopic analysis revealed objects that looked like bacteria (Figure 2.8), and these were interpreted as possible evidence for the one-time existence of primitive life-forms on Mars — but the debate continues as to whether this interpretation is correct. If you have internet access, you can find out about the latest developments on the NASA web page which can be accessed via the S194 ROUTES gateway:

http://www.jpl.nasa.gov/snc/

● Plate 2.46b shows a meteorite being carefully collected using ultra-clean conditions. Suggest a reason for taking this care.

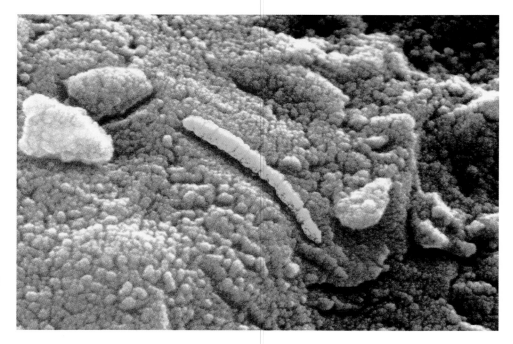

Figure 2.8 Are these microscopic fossils of primitive bacteria-like organisms on this meteorite from Mars?

○ If a meteorite is to be analysed for evidence of conditions outside the Earth (e.g. for evidence of primitive life-forms) it is important not to contaminate it with substances, including bacteria, that originate on Earth.

Most meteors and the smallest meteorites (micrometeorites) are rocky debris left over from comets. **Comets**, referred to in the introduction to Part 2 of *IC*, are bodies a few kilometres across, consisting largely of water ice and rocky particles. They are leftovers from the formation of the Solar System and orbit mainly beyond Pluto. When they stray into the inner Solar System some of the ice evaporates giving rise to enormous tails, sometimes giving spectacular sights in the night sky, such as comet Hale–Bopp did in 1997 (see Figure 2.9).

2.6 Chapter summary

The essential points of Chapter 2 are as follows.

1   The Earth is one of nine planets orbiting the Sun.

2   The Sun, planets and associated bodies make up the Solar System.

3   The Solar System is thought to have been formed from a disc of gas and dust orbiting the Sun — the solar nebula.

4   The planets in the Solar System (excluding Pluto) can be classified as either terrestrial or giant planets.

5   To maintain any circular motion, a centripetal (i.e. inwardly directed) force is required.

6   The orbital motions of planets and satellites are maintained by the force of gravity.

7   Space exploration has vastly increased our knowledge of the planets.

8   The surfaces of planets and satellites are moulded by many processes.

9   Meteorites can provide information about the surfaces of other planets (notably Mars), and about conditions during the formation of the Solar System.

10 Comets are icy–rocky debris left over from the formation of the Solar System.

11 Large numbers can be written in compact form using scientific notation.

Figure 2.9   The comet Hale–Bopp, in 1997.

2.7 End-of-chapter questions

Question 2.1   The Earth lies 150 million km from the Sun. Using scientific notation, write this distance in metres. ◄

Question 2.2   List the main characteristics of the terrestrial planets which distinguish them from the giant planets. ◄

Question 2.3   Comets are described as icy–rocky bodies left over from the formation of the Solar System. Write two or three sentences saying where in the Solar System comets must have formed, explaining your reasoning. ◄

Question 2.4   Some communications satellites are *geostationary*; that is, they remain always above the same point on the Earth's surface. In a few sentences, suggest an explanation of how it is possible for such satellites to remain in such a position. ◄

Question 2.5   Imagine you are talking to a friend who has seen a news report of a space probe being launched to another planet. On learning that the project has cost millions of dollars and taken over ten years to reach this stage, your friend wonders why it cost so much and took so long. What would you say in explanation? ◀

Question 2.6   In 1999, the NEAR space probe went into orbit about a small asteroid in order to study it in detail. Write a few sentences outlining the particular problems that might be involved in a space mission to such a small object. ◀

Question 2.7   What features distinguish an impact crater from a volcanic crater? ◀

The night sky

3

Most of the pictures in *IC* were obtained using sophisticated modern telescopes, equipped with sensitive instruments. But there is still a lot you can learn about stars and planets using your own naked-eye observations. First, you need to understand how what you can see in the night sky varies with the time of day (daily changes) and with the date in the year (seasonal changes).

3.1   Daily and seasonal changes

Activity 3.1   The night sky (30 minutes, spread over a few hours at night)

For this activity you will need a notebook, and a night sky that is clear for a few hours. Some cloud is alright, as long as you can see a few bright stars as specified below.

As soon as it has become dark, go outside and take up an observing location that you can return to later; you could mark the spot in some way. Identify a few bright stars, and write down the time and date. It will be particularly useful to find some stars in the eastern sky, and some in the western sky — you might need to use a compass to find east and west. The stars need not be low down, close to the horizon, but in any case note (in writing) the approximate positions of the stars in the east with respect to any buildings, trees, or hills in the east, and likewise for the stars in the west.

Return to your observing position about an hour later. Note the way the stars appear to have moved since you last observed them. Allow another hour to pass, and record how the stars have continued to move. Feel free to continue your observations at further hourly intervals. ◄

The outcome of Activity 3.1 is in accord with your experience of how the Sun and Moon appear to move in the course of a day — rising in the east, reaching their highest when in the south (in the north if you live in the Southern Hemisphere), and setting in the west. What is the cause of the daily east-to-west motion? We will postpone answering this question until we have posed two other questions that can be answered at the same time, as follows.

Suppose that you were to return to your observing position *at the same time of night* a few weeks later. What would you *then* observe? It would be nice if you could make this observation, but we can't wait for a few weeks, and so we give you the answer. The stars in the east will be higher in the sky, and the stars in the west will be lower — some might even have set. This means that if, for example, you go out at 22.00 hours, the positions of the stars will depend on the date — the stellar sky at a given time is *not* the same on all dates i.e. there are seasonal changes. Why is this so?

Suppose now that there is a bright planet in the sky, for example Mars. Does Mars appear to move like the stars, or in some different way?

In answering these three questions, the *general* ideas presented apply to any location on the Earth's surface, but the *details* vary according to the latitude of the location. In what follows it has been assumed that the latitude is what can be loosely described as any mid-latitude in the Northern Hemisphere. This will include Europe and North America.

Figure 3.1 shows a plan view of short segments of the orbits of the Earth and Mars as viewed from above the North Pole side of the Earth. Position (1) shows the Earth and Mars at the same moment at one end of each segment, and position (2) shows the Earth and Mars at the other end of the segment, three weeks later. Note that the size of both planets has been greatly exaggerated. Mars' orbit is not quite in the Earth's orbital plane, but we can ignore that for present purposes. The stars are *much* too far off to show in this diagram, but we can show their directions. We show the directions to stars A and B, chosen for convenience so that they lie in or near the plane of the Earth's orbit. On the scale of Figure 3.1, these directions do not change appreciably as the Earth orbits the Sun — this is because the stars are much further off than the size of the Earth's orbit. Therefore, the two direction lines to star A are parallel, and so are the direction lines to star B.

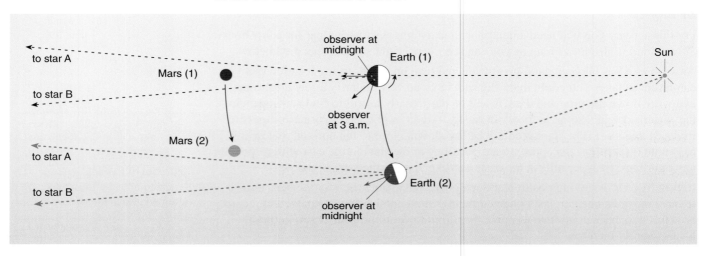

Figure 3.1 Earth, Mars and the directions to stars A and B at two different dates.

An observer, such as yourself, is shown at the location marked. This is on the spherical surface of the Earth, at some mid-latitude in the Northern Hemisphere. The arrow pointing from the observer, directly away from the Earth, is approximately in the plane of the Earth's orbit, and is *always* in the southerly direction from the observer, as illustrated in Figure 3.2. Note that Figure 3.2 is from a different viewpoint from that in Figure 3.1 — if we regard Figure 3.1 as a plan view, then Figure 3.2 is an elevation view, i.e. from the side.

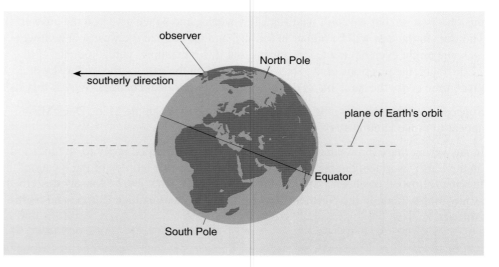

Figure 3.2 The southerly direction for the observer in Figure 3.1 (from a different viewpoint).

Returning to Figure 3.1, if you imagine yourself to be the observer, looking outwards in the southerly direction, then west is always to the right of the arrow and east to the left. At the observer's midnight the arrow points in the opposite direction to the Sun. With the Earth and Mars in the positions marked (1) Mars is in the southerly direction at midnight, star A is slightly to the west of Mars, and star B is slightly to the east. The Earth rotates anticlockwise once a day. Therefore, three hours later, the Earth's rotation has carried the observer's southerly direction around to the orientation shown at 3 a.m. in Figure 3.1. Mars and the stars A and B are no longer in the southerly direction, but in a south-westerly direction. Later they will set in the west (earlier, well before midnight, they will have risen in the east).

It is therefore the rotation of the Earth that causes the stars to rise in the east and set in the west. This applies to Mars and the other planets too. The Earth's rotation also causes the Sun to rise in the east and set in the west.

⬤ At the observer's noon, in what direction would the arrow be pointing?

◯ The arrow would then point *at* the Sun, the observer and the arrow having been carried around into this alignment by the Earth's rotation.

On the day following configuration (1) in Figure 3.1, the Earth has moved only a short distance around its orbit, so the configuration is not very different. Consequently Mars and the stars are seen in much the same directions as at the corresponding times on the preceding night. Three weeks later the Earth and Mars have reached the positions marked (2). At midnight local time, Mars and the stars are now to the west of the observer's southerly direction. Moreover, the motion of Mars around its orbit has changed its position with respect to the stars. Several months later these stars will be more or less in the same direction as the Sun, and will not be visible in the night sky.

A year later (365.3 days) the Earth is back at (1) in Figure 3.1, but though the stars will appear to be in the same directions as before, Mars will not be at the same position — its orbital period is 687 days, so it will be on the far side of the Sun.

This example of Mars and the stars should suffice to show you the reasons for

• the daily east-to-west motion of celestial objects across the sky

• the motion of the planets against the patterns formed by the background of stars

• the different appearance of the sky from one season to the next.

3.1.1 Lunar phases and eclipses

The Moon also rises in the east and sets in the west. Figure 3.3a (overleaf) shows a plan view of the Moon's orbit around the Earth as seen from above the North Pole side of the Earth. Note that the Moon's orbit lies in nearly the same plane as the Earth's orbit around the Sun. On this scale the Sun is so far off that we can show its light as sweeping across the Earth–Moon system in parallel lines. The sizes of the Earth and the Moon have been exaggerated ten times with respect to the orbit size. When the Moon is in any of the positions in Figure 3.3a then the anticlockwise rotation of the Earth causes its rising and setting, as for the other celestial bodies.

The appearance of the Moon as seen from the Earth depends on the position in its orbit at which the Moon lies. Four positions are shows in Figure 3.3a, labelled 1–4. In position '1' the Moon is in roughly the same direction as the Sun. The side facing us

Figure 3.3 (a) The Moon in its orbit around the Earth. (b) The Moon as seen from the Earth in the positions 2–4 in (a). Note that the drawings in (b) are inverted as in some astronomical telescopes.

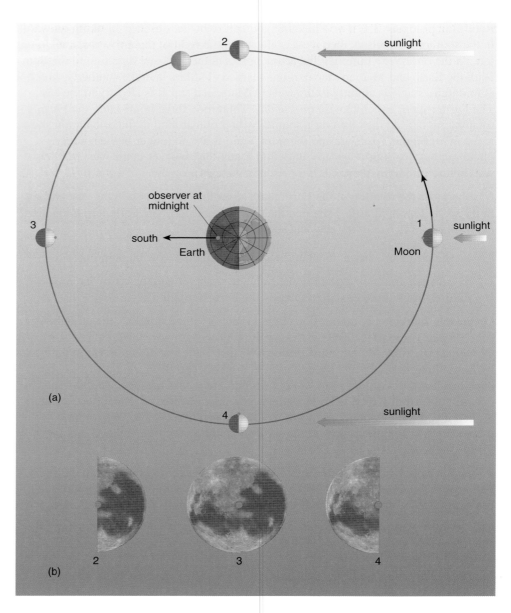

is dark so the Moon cannot be seen at all. This is the moment of the new Moon. At position '2' the Moon is half-full (first quarter), at '3' it is full, and at '4' it is again half-full (last quarter). Then it is back to new again. Each particular shape of the illuminated Moon as we see it is called a **lunar phase**, and those in positions 2–4 are shown in Figure 3.3b. Thus, new Moon is a particular phase, as is full Moon, and so on. The *average* time between successive new Moons is 29.53 days. This is called the **lunar month**, distinct from the calendar month. It varies slightly because of irregularities in the lunar orbit, but it is never as short as 29.0 days.

🌑 What is the only calendar month in which it is impossible to have two new Moons?

🌕 February — even in a leap year there are only 29.0 days in February.

With an orbital period of only 29.53 days the Moon moves appreciably around its orbit from one night to the next. For example, suppose that on a particular night the

Moon is in position '2' i.e. half-full. For an observer at their midnight the Moon will be setting on the western horizon. At midnight the following night the Moon will be in the position shown left of '2' in Figure 3.3. It will be distinctly greater than half-full and will have moved eastwards so that it is not as close to the western horizon.

In Figure 3.3a the dot on the Moon indicates a particular feature on the surface — it does not matter which one. The important point is that this dot is always facing the Earth. The Moon rotates in just the right way for it to keep the same face to the Earth. It was only in 1959 that the far side was revealed, by the USSR spacecraft Lunik III.

You might think from Figure 3.3a that at every new Moon there is a **solar eclipse** i.e. that the Moon will be seen to block the Sun from some part of the Earth's surface. That this does not normally happen is because the Moon's orbit is not quite in the same plane as the Earth's orbit. This is shown in Figure 3.4. A solar eclipse will not occur for the new Moon configuration in Figure 3.4a. However, the orientation of the lunar orbit is not fixed, and it can sometimes be as in Figure 3.4b. If the Moon is also at the new Moon position then there will be a solar eclipse. A solar eclipse is illustrated in more detail in Figure 3.5. This shows the situation at one instant. The umbral shadow is the name given to the shadow cast on the Earth from within which the Sun is completely blocked. This reveals the solar corona (Figure 1.3, Plates 1.1 and 1.2). The penumbral shadow is the name given to the shadow from within which the Sun is partly blocked — some of the bright surface is visible. The orbital motion of the Moon and the rotation of the Earth cause the umbral shadow to travel across

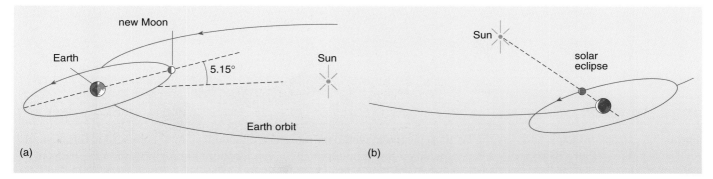

Figure 3.4 The orbit of the Moon (a) with solar eclipses not possible, (b) with a solar eclipse if the Moon is in the new Moon position.

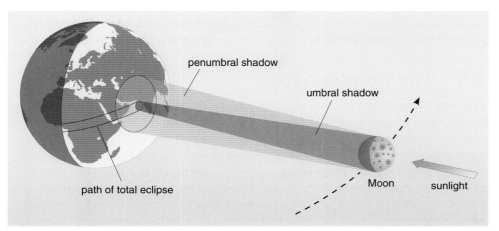

Figure 3.5 A total solar eclipse.

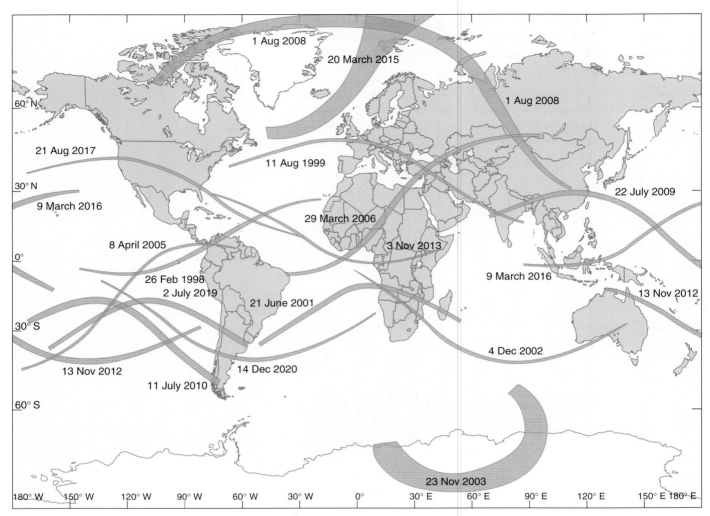

Figure 3.6 Tracks of totality for total solar eclipses 1998–2020.

the Earth, typically at well over the speed of sound, so total eclipses are rather short lived, typically a few minutes at any given location. Figure 3.6 shows the paths of totality for solar eclipses from 1998 to 2020.

The Earth also casts a shadow into space, and it is possible for this to fall on the Moon (Figure 1.6). This results in a *lunar* eclipse. If the Moon finds itself in the centre of the Earth's shadow the Moon becomes very dim, but it does not disappear because some light is bent through the Earth's atmosphere and reaches the Moon, giving it a faint coppery colour.

3.2 The planisphere

Now that you have met the reasons for the daily and seasonal changes in the sky we can turn to sky maps. Some daily newspapers publish sky maps each month which show the night sky at one particular time in the evening. We have gone one step better than this and provided you with a **planisphere**. This is a device that enables you to display a map of the night sky at any date or time. However, so that the planisphere may be used in any year, the Moon and planets are not shown on it.

 Why are the Moon and planets not shown?

The Moon and planets are excluded because, as explained for Mars in the previous section, they move against the fixed patterns formed by the stars, and do not return to the same positions on a given date every year.

Figure 3.7 shows a planisphere rather similar to the one we have sent you. It will help you to understand its operation if you have your planisphere to hand. You can see that the planisphere consists of two discs. On the lower disc there is a star map showing all the brighter stars that can ever be visible at the latitude to which the planisphere applies. This latitude is printed on the upper disc. If it is 51.5° North (the latitude of London), then it is useful from about 46° North to 57° North, which spans all but the most northerly part of the UK mainland. The lines connecting some of these stars are to help you to pick out **constellations** (star patterns). On the upper disc there is an aperture. This reveals the stars that are in the sky at particular dates and times. The edge of this aperture is the horizon, and 'S' marks the point due south on the horizon. If you face south and hold the planisphere above your head, with S towards the south, then 'Eastern Horizon' denotes your eastern horizon, and 'Western Horizon' denotes your western horizon. North is behind you.

To find the particular dates and times to which the sky in the aperture corresponds, you have to use the scales around the edges of the discs. On the lower disc are the dates through the year, and on the upper disc is the time of day. The sky in the aperture corresponds to *all* the dates and times that line up. Thus, in Figure 3.7, the sky is as at noon on 12 June, or 13.00 (1.00 p.m.) on 28 May, and so on. Of course, the Sun will be in the sky at these times so the stars will be blotted out by the blue sky.

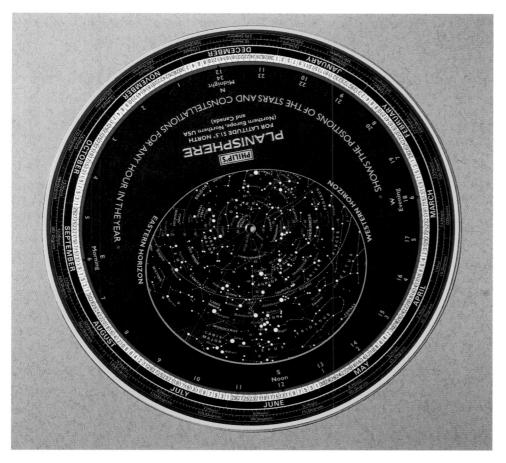

Figure 3.7 A planisphere.

On what date does Figure 3.7 show the sky at midnight?

Figure 3.7 shows the sky at midnight on 12 December.

Note that the times given by the planisphere include *no* adjustment for summer time (daylight saving time). Thus, in the UK in the summer you have to add an hour to the planisphere times to get British Summer Time.

Strictly, the times given by the planisphere are in what is called local mean solar time of the observer. For example, when the Sun is near its highest in the sky for that day, the local mean solar time is noon. But at locations to the east, noon was earlier, and to the west it will be later i.e. it depends on longitude. However, from any longitude in the UK it is sufficiently accurate to regard the time on the planisphere as Greenwich Mean Time. In the USA, it is sufficiently accurate to regard the time on the planisphere as the local zone times e.g. Eastern Standard Time in the east. In some other countries or regions, even when daylight saving time is *not* in force, the civil time kept there can be about an hour ahead of local solar time. In effect there is some daylight saving time in winter, and even more in summer. This is the case in some countries in continental Europe.

Activity 3.2   Using the planisphere (30 minutes)

For this activity you will need your planisphere. In reading times from the planisphere, estimate them to the nearest 10 minutes.

1   On your planisphere find the constellation Orion. At top left you will see a star named Betelgeuse ('betel-jers'). Set the planisphere so that Betelgeuse is on the eastern horizon. This is when the disc representing the star is bisected by the horizon. Read off the time at which this occurs on 1 January, 1 April, 1 July, and 1 October.

2   Now hold the upper disc of the planisphere and rotate the lower disc anticlockwise. This simulates the passage of time during a day. Record what happens to Betelgeuse. Include the times at which it is highest in the sky, and at which it sets, on 1 January, 1 April, 1 July, and 1 October.

3   Deduce on which of the dates 1 January, 1 April, 1 July, and 1 October, Betelgeuse is *actually* visible for the longest time.

4   Find the Plough, rotate the lower disc anticlockwise, and record what happens.

5   Lift the upper disc of the planisphere and find the star Canopus near the edge of the disc. Rotate the upper disc and note whether this star ever rises. ◀

Further advice on using the planisphere will probably be found on the back of it.

3.3   A gallery of celestial objects

In Activity 3.3 you will be asked to find a variety of celestial objects in the real sky. You will need to find a place where you can observe the night sky safely, away from bright lights and preferably not too close to tall trees or buildings — and you will need a clear night! If you have binoculars or a telescope, then that will enhance Activity 3.3, but neither is essential. You will be using your planisphere, and Figure 3.8 supplements it by presenting more detailed maps of some of the brightest constellations.

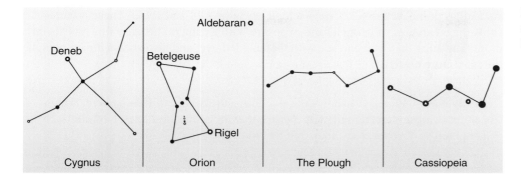

Figure 3.8 Some of the brightest constellations visible from the Northern Hemisphere.

Activity 3.3 Observing the night sky (30 minutes)

For this activity you need the planisphere, torch, notebook and pen. Jot down notes of what you see — we will return to these observations on several occasions throughout the rest of the course.

From your chosen observing position, spend a few minutes looking around the night sky and letting your eyes adapt to darkness. Try to identify some of the main constellations, using the planisphere set to your date and time. The following guidelines apply to latitudes of about 40° to 60° North, which includes the UK.

- The Plough and Cassiopeia are visible all year round in the night sky, somewhere between overhead and low in the north, depending on the time and date (see planisphere).

- Orion is prominent in the south in the winter night sky but not visible in summer.

- Cygnus is high in the night sky around midnight during the summer.

Try to find the Pleiades, a group of several bright stars very close together, north-west from Orion (see planisphere), best seen in autumn but visible for much of the rest of the year. They are sometimes known as the 'Seven Sisters' — on a clear dark night you may be able to pick out seven stars, or even more if your vision is exceptional and the sky is very dark and clear.

Notice that the stars are not all equally bright. They also have different colours: some are bluish–white, while others have a reddish tinge. The colours are less obvious if you are observing near a town where the glow of street lights spoils your view, but using binoculars can help.

On a clear winter night, you may be able to see that the middle object in Orion's Sword (below the three diagonal stars in Figure 3.8) is actually not a star but a **nebula** — a fuzzy patch of light rather than a sharp pin-point.

Look for the Milky Way, a faint milky band of light that crosses the sky through Cygnus and Cassiopeia and passes close to the red star Betelgeuse in Orion.

At certain times you will be able to see the Moon, and you might be able to spot some of the planets. Recall that these objects are not shown on the planisphere because their positions with respect to the constellations change according to where they, and the Earth, are in the Solar System (Figure 3.1). The monthly sky maps printed in some newspapers show the current positions of observable planets.

As a continuation and extension of Activity 3.1, you might like to note the positions of the constellations at different times during the same night, at the same time on different nights, and how the positions of any planets change relative to the constellations. ◀

As well as doing Activity 3.3, have a look at Plates 1.14 and 1.15a. These pictures show the advantage of using a time-exposure with a camera, because this reveals far more faint stars than you can see with the unaided eye, and also shows the colours of the stars more clearly.

> **Study Note**   Plate 1.14 shows the sky above the Southern Hemisphere, which cannot be observed from the UK. Notice that the scales on Plates 1.14 and 1.15 are given in degrees as explained in Section 1.3.

3.4   Chapter summary

The essential points of Chapter 3 are as follows.

1   What we can see in the night sky depends on the time of day and the date in the year. There is a daily east-to-west motion, and a seasonal east-to-west drift at the same time on successive dates.

2   The planets and the Moon appear to move slowly against the fixed patterns (constellations) of the stellar background.

3   Solar eclipses occur when the Moon's orbit has just the right orientation, and when, at the same time, the Moon is between the Earth and the Sun.

4   A planisphere is a device that shows the stars visible at any date and time from a given latitude on Earth.

5   A wide variety of celestial objects can be seen with the unaided eye.

3.5   End-of-chapter questions

Question 3.1   Orion is in the southerly sky at midnight on New Year's Day. Where will it be with respect to the Sun six months later? Use a sketch to support your answer. ◀

Question 3.2   Sketch the lunar phases midway between each position from 1 to 4 in Figure 3.3a. ◀

Question 3.3   In what sense does the Moon have a far side, but does not have a dark side? ◀

Question 3.4   In the skies visible from the Southern Hemisphere the Milky Way crosses the region of the Southern Cross. Examine Plate 1.14 and make a reasonable guess as to the nature of the Milky Way. Justify your guess. ◀

Observing stars

4

This chapter is about the ways astronomers can observe and study stars and other objects in the sky.

4.1   Constellations and stellar distances

In Activity 3.3 we referred to various constellations. These groupings and names of stars owe rather more to imagination than reality. Those shown in Figure 3.8 and on the planisphere have names that date back to ancient Greek civilization and are mostly named after characters in Greek mythology, whereas individual stars often have names of Arab origin (e.g. Altair, Deneb). Oriental civilizations have tended to see the stars in smaller groups and name them differently. Southern-hemisphere constellations have acquired European names relatively recently (for example there is one called the Microscope).

Nowadays astronomers use constellation names only as a convenient way to refer to different parts of the sky and different stars. Stars are named according to an internationally agreed code, in which an abbreviated form of the constellation name is preceded by a Greek letter, with α (alpha) usually being the star in the constellation that seems brightest from Earth. The remaining stars in the constellation are then named β (beta), γ (gamma), δ (delta)… in descending order of brightness as seen from Earth. The actual constellations themselves are not studied by astronomers as they are not real groupings of stars i.e. the stars in a constellation are not usually nearest neighbours in space.

4.1.1   Distances to the stars

The true nature of constellations becomes more obvious when we look at how stars are actually distributed in space. To do this, we need to find the distances to the stars. In principle at least, measuring such distances is simpler than you might think.

Near the start of Chapter 1 we discussed the point that other stars look so much fainter than the Sun because they are so much further away. Astronomers can make use of this to deduce the actual distances to stars. There is one important observation that makes this easier: namely, that *stars which are the same size and colour give out the same amount of light*. So if astronomers observe two stars of exactly the same colour, they can start by *assuming* they are the same size and therefore they must be giving out the same amount of light. If one looks fainter, it must be further away. By measuring the amount of light entering a telescope from each star, astronomers can work out just how much further away one star is than the other. Figure 4.1 shows the principle. Stars A and B give out the same amount of light, but B is at twice the distance of A so its light is more spread out by the time it reaches the observer on Earth. Four times as much light from A enters the telescope (or eye) and so A appears four times brighter. If B were at three times the distance of A, A would appear nine times brighter, and if B were at ten times the distance of A, A would appear one hundred times brighter, and so on.

○ If star B were at five times the distance of star A, how much brighter would A appear?

○ Star A would appear 25 times brighter than star B.

● What is a general rule describing how the apparent brightness of a star diminishes with distance?

○ The general rule is that the apparent brightness diminishes as the *square* of the distance (the distance multiplied by itself). That is, if the distance is multiplied by 2, the apparent brightness is reduced by 2×2 (= 4). If the distance is multiplied by 5, then the apparent brightness is reduced by 5×5 (= 25) i.e. such a star has 1/25 the apparent brightness of a similar star lying at one-fifth of its distance.

Figure 4.1 Light from a more distant star B is more spread out so the star appears fainter than an identical star A nearby.

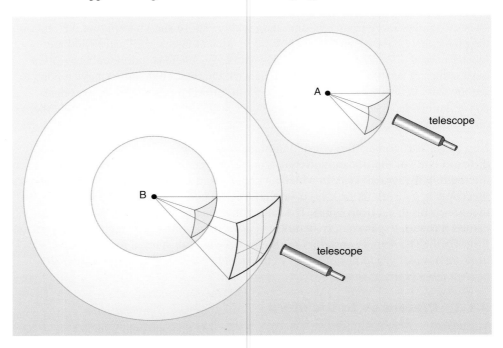

In practice it is not quite so easy to measure distance, because some stars are the same colour but different sizes and so give out different amounts of light — but the general principle of 'faint means far' underlies most of the techniques for measuring distances.

As you might imagine from comparing their appearance to the Sun, other stars are at *very* large distances from us. The nearest star to the Sun, known as Proxima Centauri ('proxima' is Latin for nearest, and the star is in the constellation Centaurus) is at a distance of about 4×10^{13} km, and other stars are tens, hundreds or even thousands of times further.

> **Study Note** Note the slight change in the name of the constellation (Centauri) when put next to the name of a particular star. This is in accord with the rules of Latin grammar!

When we are dealing with distances to stars, using kilometres leads to very large numbers which can be awkward to handle, even using scientific notation. Astronomers therefore sometimes express large distances in terms of the **light year** (abbreviated as ly). One light year (1 ly) is the distance that light (and all other types of electromagnetic radiation) travels through space in one year, and is equal to 9.46×10^{12} km (nearly ten million million kilometres). Bearing in mind that light travels extremely fast —300 000 kilometres per second, about 660 million miles per hour — you can see why the light year is a very long distance. Proxima Centauri is about 4.2 ly from us.

> **Study Note** Another unit of distance, which you might see in some astronomy books, is the parsec (pc). 1 parsec is 3.09×10^{13} km or 3.26 ly. This unit is preferred by stellar and galactic astronomers. This is because of the way it is defined, but we have no space to go into that.

> **Study Note** Notice that, despite their names sounding a bit like years or seconds, **a light year and a parsec are both distances not times**, so phrases such as 'that happened light years ago' or 'we'll be there in a couple of parsecs' heard in bad science fiction movies are nonsense.

From Plate 1.16 onwards in Part 1 of *IC* many of the pictures have scales given in light years. To remind you how vast the distances are, it can be instructive to write the distances in kilometres as well, by multiplying the distance in ly by 9.46×10^{12}. To do this on a calculator, you need to use the button marked EE or EXP, which means 'times ten to the power of'. So to enter 9.46×10^{12} you key in 9.46, then press EE or EXP, then key in 12. Your calculator display should then look something like one of those in Figure 4.2 — different calculators display scientific notation in slightly different ways. Then you can type in the number of light years and multiply in the normal way. For example, multiplying by 228 (the distance to α Cas in ly) gives the distance in kilometres as 2.15688×10^{15} (approximately 2.16×10^{15}).

Figure 4.2 Calculator displays showing 9.46×10^{12}.

> **Study Note** A common mistake is to type in 9.46×10 before pressing the EE button and typing 12. This first multiplies the number by ten, so you end up with an answer that is ten times too big.

⬤ The distance to γ Cas (gamma Cassiopeiae) is 613 ly. What is this in km?

◯ $(613 \times 9.46 \times 10^{12})$ km $= 5.79898 \times 10^{15}$ km, which is approximately 5.80×10^{15} km.

To get from a distance in kilometres to one in light years, you divide by 9.46×10^{12}. On a calculator, enter the distance in kilometres (using the EE or EXP button as necessary), then press the '÷' button before entering 9.46×10^{12} as before.

⬤ The distance to δ Cas (delta Cas) is 9.4×10^{14} km. What is this distance in ly?

◯ The calculator might display 9.9×10^{1} i.e. the distance is 99 ly, or it might give 99 directly. (In fact it would have showed a lot more digits, but there are only two in 9.4, and so only the first two digits in the answer are meaningful.)

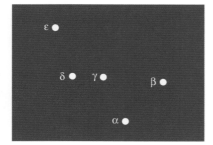

Figure 4.3 The five brightest stars in Cassiopeia.

4.1.2 Constellations in three dimensions

As you probably saw in Activity 3.3, the five bright stars that make the W of Cassiopeia appear quite close together in the sky (see Figure 4.3). Table 4.1 lists these stars in decreasing order of brightness as observed from Earth and gives their approximate distances. From Table 4.1 you can see that the most distant star, γ Cas (gamma Cas) lies eleven times further away than β Cas (Caph), the closest. Figure 4.4 shows a simple three-dimensional model of these five stars. Viewed from our particular direction they appear to be quite closely grouped in a W shape, but from other directions they would appear to be unrelated to one another — as indeed they are.

Table 4.1 The five brightest stars in Cassiopeia.

| Star | | Approximate distance | |
International name	Traditional name	in kilometres	in light years
α Cas	Schedar	2.2×10^{15}	228
β Cas	Caph	5.1×10^{14}	54
γ Cas	–	5.8×10^{15}	613
δ Cas	Ruchbah	9.4×10^{14}	99
ε Cas	Segin	4.2×10^{15}	442

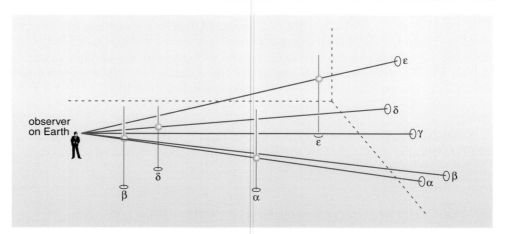

Figure 4.4 A three-dimensional view of the five brightest stars in Cassiopeia. Note that γ Cas is so far to the right, that only its apparent position can be shown on this diagram.

4.2 The colours of starlight

In Activity 3.3 and in Plates 1.14 and 1.15a, you saw that stars have different colours. These colours provide astronomers with useful information about the temperature of the stars' photospheres. Activity 4.1 illustrates how this comes about.

Activity 4.1 Getting warmer (10 minutes)

For this activity, you need an electric bar (not blow) heater or the ring of an electric cooker (not the 'halogen' type). Switch on, and hold your hand several centimetres away from the heating element (do not touch it!). Notice what you feel as the heating element warms up and also notice how its appearance changes. A dark room helps. ◀

At first, nothing much seems to happen in Activity 4.1. Then you begin to feel heat being given out, but there is still no change in the appearance of the heating element. As you feel the element getting hotter, it begins to glow, first a dull dark red, then brighter until it eventually becomes a bright orange–red and very hot. What you have experienced is an important connection between the temperature of an object and the electromagnetic radiation that it gives out (mostly visible light and infrared in this case). You can extend the example a bit further. Think of a filament light bulb; it is much hotter than a heating element, and glows almost white. A low-power torch bulb is intermediate between the two — it glows yellow–white.

In principle then, astronomers can judge the temperatures of stars (and, indeed, any objects that give out light) simply by observing their colours. In practice they split up the light into its different colours and compare the amounts of each. One way to do this is to send the light through a prism (a triangular block of glass), which splits up white light into a rainbow of colours (known as a spectrum) as shown in the bottom part (continuous spectrum) of Plate 1.4.

The star Betelgeuse, in the constellation of Orion, is orange while Rigel (also in Orion) is blue–white (see Plate 1.15a). Which star is hotter?

The orange colour of Betelgeuse shows that it is fairly cool while Rigel's blue–white colour shows it is hotter.

4.2.1 Colour, temperature and wavelength

You might sum up the connection between temperature and electromagnetic radiation as 'the hotter the brighter, the hotter the whiter'. In fact, this snappy summary is a bit of an over-simplification, because very hot objects give out more blue light than any other colour so they appear blue rather than white. And *very* hot objects give out a lot of ultraviolet radiation and even X-rays as well as visible light that is predominantly blue. At the other extreme, even cool objects give out some electromagnetic radiation, only it nearly all consists of infrared, radio and microwaves — invisible to our eyes, but detectable by suitable instruments as illustrated in Figure 4.5.

Figure 4.5 Infrared radiation detected from a shopper with red showing the warmer parts and blue the cooler parts.

41

A more exact summary would be to say that *all* objects give out electromagnetic radiation; the hotter an object is, the more electromagnetic radiation it gives altogether and the more it gives out at short wavelengths in particular. As well as using words, this can be shown on a graph such as Figure 4.6. The Sun is a yellowish–white star, with a photosphere temperature of about 5500 °C. From Figure 4.6 and your observations in Activity 3.3 you can see that our Sun is a middling sort of star. Some stars are blue–white like Rigel, with temperatures of perhaps 15 000 °C or more, while others, such as Betelgeuse, are orange in colour and relatively cool at only about 4000 °C.

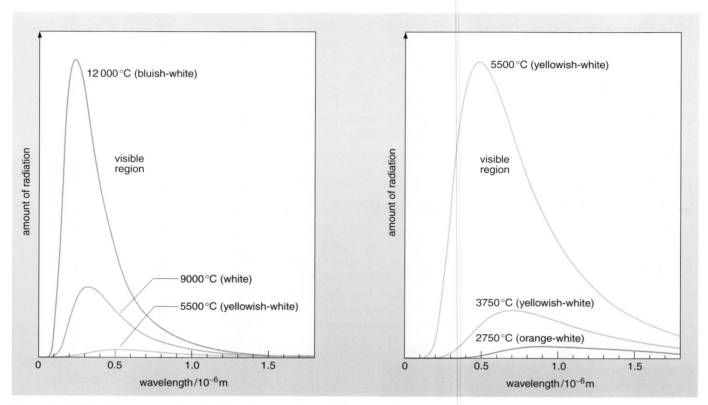

Figure 4.6 The electromagnetic radiation given out by an object at various temperatures.

 Study Note You might like to refer back to Chapter 1 and to the Introduction to *IC* to refresh your memory of types of electromagnetic radiation and their wavelength range.

 Suppose astronomers observed an object that gave out most of its radiation as X-rays. What could you say about the likely temperature of such an object?

 Since X-rays have much shorter wavelengths than visible light, they are generally given out by *very* hot objects. (For example, you saw in Chapter 1 and Plate 1.7 that the Sun's corona, which gives out X-rays, has a temperature of over 1 million °C.)

As you saw in Chapter 1, we need very small numbers to write the wavelengths of most types of electromagnetic radiation. As with writing very large numbers, we can use scientific notation to make the numbers more compact. Table 4.2 shows how we can write very small numbers by extending the pattern from Table 2.3. It is perhaps surprising to see that $10^0 = 1$, but that follows inevitably if we continue the pattern downwards, dividing by 10 each time. For small numbers, notice that the power is the same as the number of steps from the decimal point (*not* the number of zeros after the point). For example, 0.0001 is 10^{-4}, and the 1 is in the fourth place after the point. Notice that the wavelengths on Figure 4.6 are given in scientific notation.

Table 4.2   Powers of ten including small numbers.

	continue up for smaller numbers	
0.0001 =	1/10000 =	10^{-4}
0.001 =	1/1000 =	10^{-3}
0.01 =	1/100 =	10^{-2}
0.1 =	1/10 =	10^{-1}
1 =	1 =	10^0
10 =	10 =	10^1
100 =	10×10 =	10^2
1000 =	$10 \times 10 \times 10$ =	10^3
10 000 =	$10 \times 10 \times 10 \times 10$ =	10^4
100 000 =	$10 \times 10 \times 10 \times 10 \times 10$ =	10^5
1000 000 =	$10 \times 10 \times 10 \times 10 \times 10 \times 10$ =	10^6
	continue down for larger numbers	

Using powers of ten as shown in Table 4.2, small numbers are written in scientific notation in just the same way as large numbers i.e. with one figure before the decimal point. For example, 0.0003 is written as 3×10^{-4}, and 0.0076 is written 7.6×10^{-3}. To enter numbers like this on a calculator, you need to use the 'change sign' button (labelled +/−) *not* the minus button, so to enter 7.6×10^{-3} you would type in 7.6 then press EE, then +/− and then 3.

⬤ Visible light ranges in wavelength from about 0.000 0004 m (violet light) to 0.000 0007 m (red light). Write these wavelengths in scientific notation.

◯ 0.000 0004 m is 4×10^{-7} m and 0.000 0007 m is 7×10^{-7} m.

⬤ Three wavelengths are labelled on Figure 4.6 using scientific notation. Rewrite these wavelengths using ordinary notation.

◯ 0.5×10^{-6} m is 0.000 0005 m. 1×10^{-6} m is 0.000 001 m. Also 1.5×10^{-6} m is 0.000 0015 m (i.e. $1.5 \times 0.000 001$ m).

4.2.2   Wavelength and composition

Sending starlight through a prism can provide even more information than just temperature. If the light is spread out finely enough, as in Plate 1.6, narrow dark **spectral lines** can be seen where certain colours of light (certain wavelengths) are very faint or missing. This means that if an image of a star were to be obtained at the wavelength of one of these lines it will appear rather dark. The lines depend on the substances that make up the outer parts of the star, so by studying starlight in detail astronomers can not only deduce a star's temperature but what it is made of. Stars are made largely of hydrogen with small amounts of other substances. As you will see in Chapter 5, astronomers use spectral lines in other important ways as well as determining which substances are present.

4.3   Chapter summary

The essential points of Chapter 4 are as follows.

1   Stars appear to be arranged in constellations but these do not represent real groupings of stars.

2   By comparing the apparent brightness of stars, astronomers can deduce their distances; the fainter a star appears, the greater its distance.

3   The light year is the distance light travels through space in a year; stars typically lie many light years from one another and from Earth.

4   The colours of stars indicate their temperatures; blue–white stars are hottest, while reddish stars are not as hot.

5   Spectral lines give information about the substances that make up a star.

6   Small numbers can be written in a compact way using scientific notation with negative numbers for the powers of ten.

4.4   End-of-chapter questions

Question 4.1   Plate 1.14 shows the four stars that make up the Southern Cross. What can you deduce about the temperatures and likely distances of these four stars just by looking at this image? (On a photograph such as this, the images of brighter stars appear larger than those of faint stars. This is an artefact — the images should all be points of light.) ◀

Question 4.2   In the introduction to *IC*, the chart showing the electromagnetic spectrum is labelled 0.000 001 metres and 0.000 001 *millionths* of a metre. Rewrite these numbers in scientific notation. ◀

Star birth and death

In this chapter we turn our attention to star formation and evolution — how stars are made, how they change with time, and what happens when they come to an end. Like Eddington's solution to the puzzle of the Sun's power supply, this story is one that astronomers have gradually pieced together. This is not easy, because we do not see stars forming and changing before our eyes — the processes involved happen far too slowly. All we have is a snapshot of a large number of stars and nebulae at one particular time, together with some knowledge of how materials behave in Earth-based experiments.

The story told in this chapter is summarized at the start of Part 1 of *IC*, and you should read that summary now. Bear in mind that the story in the summary, and as elaborated in this chapter, is supported by a great deal of evidence and experiment, and that it has been developed over many years. However, it is still in the process of being refined in the light of ever more sophisticated observations.

5.1 Making stars

As you saw in Chapters 1 and 4, the Sun is a typical star. Some stars are hotter and others less hot, but all are sustained by nuclear reactions which enable them to give out vast amounts of electromagnetic radiation over millions of years.

5.1.1 From dense cloud to protostar

Between the stars there is the so-called **interstellar medium** (ISM) — very thin gas and tiny specks of dust. Plates 1.13 and 1.14 and their captions give some idea of what the ISM is like. Some regions of the ISM are identifiable as nebulae (clouds), including the Orion nebula that you might have seen in Activity 3.3. Some regions of the ISM are hot and glow with visible light, while others are so cold that they are detectable only through the weak radio waves they emit; all are *very* much thinner than the Earth's atmosphere. Plate 3.5b (in Part 3 of *IC*) is a picture of part of the sky in the Orion region and shows something of the variety of gas clouds found in the ISM.

To form stars, a region of the ISM has to collapse in on itself under its own gravity. The regions that can do this most easily are those that are already the most dense. They are known as **molecular clouds** because they are made up of so-called molecular gas. There is nothing very mysterious about this — the Earth's atmosphere is made up of molecular gas. (Other regions of the ISM are made from gas in different forms which come about when 'ordinary' molecular gas is heated to very high temperatures.) Molecular clouds are also the coldest parts of the ISM, with temperatures of about −250 °C or even lower. They are sometimes also known as **dense clouds**, but this term is relative; they are the densest regions of the ISM but even at their densest they are about as thin as the very best vacuums that can be produced in our laboratories!

One way in which star formation can start is when gas clouds collide, since that helps to squash the gas together so that parts of the cloud begin to gravitationally contract. As each part contracts it will split into fragments, and each fragment then gravitationally contracts separately. You can picture the contraction of a single fragment as being rather like leaves or rain falling to Earth. However, whereas the fall towards the Earth's centre is halted when the Earth's surface is encountered, in the

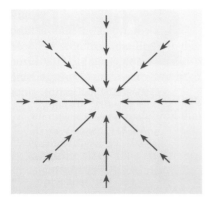

Figure 5.1 Material in a contracting cloud fragment speeds up as it falls. Each line represents the distance fallen in a given time interval.

case of the fragment the fall continues, and it is the whole fragment which 'falls' towards its centre. Like objects falling to Earth, the gas making up the molecular cloud speeds up as it 'falls' (shown schematically in Figure 5.1). In doing so it gets hotter as the gas molecules collide with each other. Each contracting fragment becomes a **protostar** — the forerunner of a proper star. It takes millions of years to get from a contracting molecular cloud to a protostar. This is because of the distances involved — a molecular cloud might typically be about 10 light years across.

 Protostars, like all objects, give out electromagnetic radiation. How would you expect this radiation to change as a protostar became hotter?

 The dominant wavelength range of the radiation would shift to shorter wavelengths. At first the very cool material would mainly emit radio waves, then microwaves as it became warmer.

5.1.2 From protostar to star

Eventually a protostar gets hot enough to give out infrared radiation. Plate 1.15b shows infrared emission from the Orion region — an area rich in star-formation. Notice that this picture is colour-coded so that white means hot and red means cool i.e. it adopts the same pattern as for visible light.

The contraction continues, and by the time the gas has fallen through a distance of a few light years it can reach temperatures of over ten million degrees Celsius i.e. 10^7 °C or more. By this time it is squashed together into a very small space — gas that was originally spread out over a few light years can be squashed into a space similar in size to the Sun. At this point, hydrogen nuclear reactions can begin in the hottest parts (the **cores**) and so the protostars become stars. Their radiation heats up the surrounding ISM, which becomes hot enough to glow and then eventually disperses.

The idea of starting from a cold thin molecular cloud to make, hot, dense bright stars might seem a bit far-fetched. What is the evidence for this scenario? One piece of evidence comes from observations like those illustrated in Plates 1.15 to 1.17 and 1.20 to 1.22a, where regions of the ISM which contain cold molecular clouds are seen also to contain bright stars and glowing gas which they have heated. (Note the different scales of these plates.)

The story is also based firmly on our understanding of how gases behave on Earth. Astronomers can use this knowledge to work out what happens to large interstellar gas clouds when they collide, and use computers to carry out many step-by-step calculations to show how the density and temperature change with time. The video sequence *Formation of protostars* shows the results of some of these computer simulations and is the basis of Activity 5.1.

Activity 5.1 Formation of protostars (20 minutes)

Study the video sequence *Formation of protostars*, and write down the key points it makes. It runs for 10 minutes and you should allow about 20 minutes to study it.

The sequence shows how computer calculations can predict the changes of density and temperature of molecular clouds that contract following a collision.

This video sequence was produced for the course S281 *Astronomy and planetary science* and contains a few terms that will probably be unfamiliar to you. Distances are given in parsecs (pc) not light years; 1 pc is 3.26 ly, so 3 pc (the cloud diameter) is roughly 10 ly. Near the end of the sequence, sizes of protostars are given in 'astronomical units'. An astronomical unit is the distance from Earth to Sun, about 1.5×10^8 km. A light year is 6.32×10^4 astronomical units.

At various points, 'solar masses' are mentioned. This is a convenient way of describing the masses of stars and other large objects. The Sun's mass, '1 solar mass', is 2×10^{30} kg (about 2×10^{27} tonnes), so a star of, say, 4 solar masses contains four times as much material as the Sun and its mass is 8×10^{30} kg.

The commentary refers to the colours of 'pixels'. The pixels ('picture elements') are the small coloured dots or squares that make up the image. Notice the use of colour; in these simulations colour represents density.

As you view the sequence, notice how the clumps of material collapse in on themselves, and look out for a comparison between the computer prediction and real observations of the Orion molecular cloud — the two appear very similar.

Look out for information on timescales and density. At one point the commentary states that density is 'a factor of 10^9 higher' than in the original cloud. How long has it taken to become this dense?

At a time of about 7 min 30 sec from the start, you are instructed to stop the tape and refer to 'your notes'. *Ignore* this instruction. The notes form part of the material for S281 and contain information about conditions in real molecular clouds (which are very similar to those predicted by the computer).

At a time of about 8 min 30 sec, you see another sequence which shows the formation of a multiple star system. ◄

After you have studied the video in Activity 5.1, look at Plate 1.15 again and study its caption. Notice that Plate 1.15c shows shapes which are similar to parts of the colliding clouds shown in the video sequence, but its colour coding and the scale are completely different.

5.1.3 Stars and their neighbours

The computer simulations you saw in Activity 5.1 showed that the collapsing clouds tend to break up and form *several* stars — not just one. Observations of real stars bear this out. Plates 1.17a and b show many stars apparently formed from one part of the Orion Nebula, and Plates 1.20 to 1.22a also show groups of apparently newly-formed stars. Plate 1.22b shows another cluster of stars, the Pleiades (which you may have seen in Activity 3.3). These stars are slightly older than those in Plate 1.22a, and the hot interstellar gas has dispersed from around them — the wispy material is a cloud through which the Pleiades currently happens to be passing. Plate 1.22c shows a yet older star cluster which has long lost its glowing ISM. All these clusters contain hundreds, perhaps a few thousand, stars. They are known as *open clusters*. The star clusters in Plate 3.6 each contain about a million stars, are very ancient, and are known as *globular clusters*; presumably they also each formed from a molecular cloud, though perhaps not the sort existing today.

The second simulation, shown near the end of the video sequence, showed the formation of a multiple star system consisting of a **binary star** (two stars in orbit around each other) closely associated with a third star. Binary stars are very common; the Sun, being an isolated star, is quite unusual. Some binary stars are very close together so material may flow from one of the pair to the other; Plate 1.25 shows artists' impressions of such interacting binary stars.

5.1.4 Discs and planets

Near the start of the video sequence in Activity 5.1 you may have noticed a mention of rotating discs of gas and dust forming as the molecular cloud collapsed. Studies of the behaviour of collapsing gas clouds show that some of the material will spiral towards the centre like water running down a plughole, but some will remain in orbit around the central star. Plates 1.19b and 2.1 show artists' impressions of such discs. It is thought that such discs of orbiting gas and dust will eventually yield planets.

The formation of discs around young stars suggests that planets are a natural by-product of star formation. Individual Earth-sized planets would be too small to see even with today's telescopes, but there have been several searches for discs of warm infrared-emitting material around nearby stars — and some of these have borne fruit with images such as that in Plate 1.19a. In November 1999 a team from Berkeley USA found other evidence for a planet orbiting another star: the star's light dimmed regularly in a way that can be explained by a giant planet passing in front of it as in Figure 5.2. Quite a few planetary systems are now known, as you will see in Chapter 6.

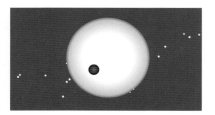

Figure 5.2   Artist's impression of a planet passing in front of the star known as HD209458.

5.2   The fate of stars

Once a star is formed, powered by nuclear reactions of hydrogen, it continues to shine steadily for many millions of years. A star fuelled by hydrogen reactions is known as a **main sequence star**. For a star like the Sun, the main sequence stage lasts about 10^{10} years (ten billion years). The heavier the star, the more rapidly it consumes its nuclear fuel, and so the hotter its photosphere and the more brightly it glows. Eventually the hydrogen in its core is exhausted. What happens next depends on the amount of material making up the star. Here we will concentrate on the more dramatic endpoints of stars' lives.

5.2.1   Red giants and white dwarfs

After exhausting its hydrogen fuel supply, a middling star, such as our Sun, goes through a few more stages of nuclear reactions involving other substances. These reactions are accompanied by the outer parts of the star swelling to hundreds of times their original size, and cooling from about 6000 °C to about 3000 °C. (The reasons for this are complex and not well understood — this is one part of the stars' lifestory that has not yet been very well worked out.) The star now appears orange in colour, but gives out a lot of light because of its large size. It is known as a **red giant** star. Plate 1.23 shows the relative sizes of the Sun and a typical red giant.

◯ According to the caption of Plate 1.23, what happens to a star after it has been a red giant?

◯ The star sheds a lot of material and becomes a **white dwarf** star (represented by a tiny white dot on the picture).

The ejected outer parts form a so-called **planetary nebula** (a confusing name, since it has nothing to do with planets). These are amongst the most spectacular objects in the sky. As you can see in Plates 1.26 and 1.27, they form shells of glowing material, each centred on a small white dwarf star. Eventually this ejected material cools and fades from view.

Betelgeuse in Orion is orange — Plate 1.15a and Plate 1.24 both show images of Betelgeuse. However, it is not a red giant, but a supergiant, evolved from a star about 20 times more massive than the Sun. Such stars have a more dramatic end.

5.2.2 Supernovae

If a star is more than about eight times the mass of the Sun, it swells and cools, with an increase in brightness, to become a **supergiant** after exhausting its hydrogen nuclear fuel supply, and its end is much more spectacular. After going rapidly through further stages of nuclear reactions, the whole star undergoes a sudden very violent explosion called a **supernova**. This is one of the few stages in a star's life that happens rapidly enough for us to see it take place. Within a matter of minutes, the entire star is ripped apart, accompanied by an enormous output of light and other electromagnetic radiation. Plate 1.28 shows a picture of a supernova alongside a picture of the same part of the sky before it happened. This supernova was at a distance of about 163 000 light years but could still be seen with the naked eye. Plate 1.29a shows the Crab Nebula, the aftermath of a supernova explosion only 4000 light years away. It was so bright that it was visible with the naked eye in daylight and was recorded by the Chinese in 1054AD.

5.2.3 Pulsars

After a supernova explosion, a small part of the original star may remain at the centre. This remnant has no more nuclear fuel and shrinks under its own gravity. It may become a **pulsar** as shown schematically in Plate 1.29b and described in its caption. As the star shrinks, it spins more rapidly. It is observed to 'pulse' because it acts rather like a lighthouse — as it rotates, its radio beam sweeps round, and we detect a sharp flash each time the beam points directly towards us. Activity 5.2 demonstrates these properties of pulsars.

Activity 5.2   Modelling pulsars (20 minutes)

To see what happens when a slowly rotating star collapses, you need a rotating stool or chair (e.g. an office chair). Sit with your arms and legs stretched out and spin slowly. Now bring your arms and legs close to your body — you will feel yourself spinning faster. An expert ice-skater can demonstrate the same effect by spinning slowly with outstretched arms, then drawing her arms close to her body to make herself spin faster. In the same way, when a rotating star becomes more compact, it spins more rapidly.

To model the 'pulsing' of a pulsar, you need a pair of scissors (preferably with straight blades and rounded ends as shown in Figure 5.3) and some Blu-Tack. Use the Blu-Tack to fix the blades open, and twirl the scissors about one shaft which is held upright

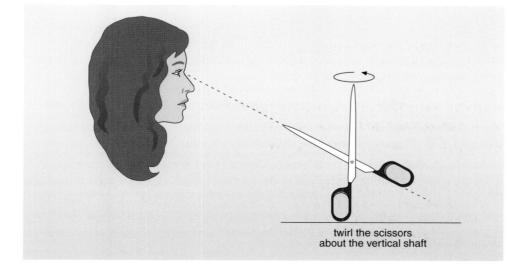

twirl the scissors
about the vertical shaft

Figure 5.3   Modelling the way we 'see' radio pulses from a pulsar.

(being careful not to stab yourself). Experiment until you find an arrangement where the slanted blade points directly at you once in each revolution. The slanted blade represents the radio beam which you can 'see' only when it is directed towards you so you observe a series of short flashes as the pulsar rotates. ◄

The first pulsar was identified by Jocelyn Bell Burnell in 1967 at Cambridge. She is presently professor of physics at the Open University.

5.2.4 Black holes

In some cases after a supernova, the central remaining part of the star collapses in on itself even further. Its gravity becomes so strong that nothing, not even light, can escape. It is known as a **black hole**. Black holes seem very mysterious objects, but their existence is predicted as a quite straightforward consequence of the way we know matter behaves — they are not science fiction. Since light cannot escape from them, they are quite difficult to observe, though not, in fact, impossible. The strong gravity of a black hole draws other material towards it. Plate 1.25b shows an artist's impression of a possible black hole near another star. As material is pulled towards the black hole, it swirls around and becomes very hot — so hot that it can give out X-rays. X-ray telescopes have detected several very compact objects that are probably black holes pulling material towards themselves.

5.2.5 Supernova remnants

As you can see from Plate 1.29a, supernova explosions can leave spectacular **supernova remnants** of ejected material which continues to glow for a long time after the explosion. Plates 1.30 and 1.31 show images of two other supernova remnants. Study these images and their captions carefully.

● A pulsar is found at the centre of each of the Vela and Crab supernova remnants, but none is found at the centre of the Cassiopeia A remnant or, indeed, in many other supernova remnants. Suggest three reasons for this (apparent) absence of a pulsar.

○ The entire star may have been disrupted in the supernova explosion, leaving nothing at the centre, or maybe the supernova explosion left a black hole rather than a pulsar, or perhaps there is a pulsar whose radio beam does not point towards us so we cannot detect it. (Another possibility is that the explosion was lopsided, propelling the pulsar out of the remnant.)

Over thousands of years, the material ejected in a supernova explosion cools and fades from view, becoming indistinguishable from the rest of the ISM. Eventually some of it might become incorporated in a region cool and dense enough to contract under its own gravity, and so the process of star formation starts all over again.

Activity 5.3 The cosmic cycle (20 minutes)

The introduction to Part 1 of *IC* summarizes the way that material is cycled through stars and the ISM and provides a diagram to illustrate this.

Make a large sketch copy of the diagram. Then go back through this chapter and try to identify images that illustrate each of the labelled stages. (Ignore 'infall from deep space' since this is neither discussed nor illustrated here nor in *IC*.) Next to each label on your sketch, note the relevant plate numbers — for example, for 'dense clouds' (i.e. molecular clouds) you could note the Orion Nebula shown in Plate 1.16 or the Trifid Nebula (Plate 1.20). ◄

5.2.6 Update

Since *IC* was written, the Hubble Space Telescope has produced many spectacular and detailed images of star formation sites, planetary nebulae and supernova remnants. If you have internet access, you can view some of these pictures (and much more!) on the Cambridge astronomy website, which has a mirror of the Hubble Space Telescope site:

http://www.ast.cam.ac.uk

This can be accessed via the S194 ROUTES gateway.

5.3 Chapter summary

The essential points of Chapter 5 are as follows.

1 Star formation begins with the contraction of a molecular cloud under gravity.

2 A contracting fragment of a cloud becomes a protostar, its central temperatures increasing until they are high enough for nuclear reactions to begin.

3 A main sequence star shines steadily for billions of years while consuming its hydrogen in nuclear reactions.

4 When its hydrogen is exhausted, a main sequence star swells to become a red giant or a supergiant.

5 A red giant ejects a planetary nebula and ends as a white dwarf.

6 A star that begins with over eight times the Sun's mass ends in a violent supernova explosion, leaving an extended remnant and possibly either a pulsar or a black hole.

7 Material ejected from stars eventually cools and may take part in further cycles of star formation.

5.4 End-of-chapter questions

Question 5.1   List the following terms in the correct order to describe the life history of a star similar to the Sun: main sequence star; white dwarf; planetary nebula; protostar; dense cloud; red giant. ◀

Question 5.2   In this chapter you met various types of nebula, exemplified by the Trifid Nebula (Plate 1.20), the Helix Nebula (Plate 1.27b) and the Crab Nebula (Plate 1.29a). For each of these, write a sentence or two describing it and saying how it illustrates part of the life history of a star. ◀

Is there life beyond the Earth?

Some scientific questions are of immediate and widespread interest, and they stir our imaginations. One of these is the subject of this chapter — is there life beyond the Earth? This question has surely been pondered ever since it was realized in antiquity that there might be celestial bodies of rock and water beyond the Earth, but it is only in the last 50 years or so that we have made significant scientific progress towards answering it. Today, the question is still unanswered, but it is the focus of intense scientific activity. This is a fast moving area, where much is still uncertain, and it is beyond reasonable doubt that significant developments will be made before we are many years into the new millennium.

A few people believe that we already *know* that there is life beyond Earth; they claim that we have been visited by aliens. Figure 6.1 shows a fanciful depiction of aliens — not as remarkably humanoid as many other representations! Though it is easy to laugh at the notion of alien visitation, it is in fact a perfectly serious question to ask whether it has actually happened. The perfectly serious answer is that there is no scientific evidence for it. The claims lack objective facts. Certainly, there are unexplained happenings, but the important word is 'unexplained', and a belief that alien visitation is the explanation is just that, a *belief*. It is always possible that tomorrow there will be a clear and obvious visitation, but this has not happened yet.

We therefore have the Earth as the one place in the whole Universe where we *know* there is life. In searching for life elsewhere we must be guided by the key features of life on Earth, and the essential conditions for life here. We therefore start in Section 6.1 with a quick look at life on our own planet. Then, in Section 6.2, we identify other bodies in the Solar System that might have been suitable for the emergence of life, or that might be suitable for supporting life today, and we ask whether life has already been found on any of them. In Section 6.3 we look beyond the Solar System, and consider how we might detect life on planets around other stars.

Figure 6.1 What life might look like on an alien world.

6.1 Life on Earth

Life on Earth today displays bewildering variety, yet all organisms in a fundamental sense are rather similar. The most familiar organisms are large ones — from elephants, blue whales and trees, down to spiders and fleas. Yet even at the small end of this size range the organism consists of a large number of what are called cells — about 10^6 in the case of a flea. Other organisms consist of just a single cell — bacteria are a widespread example. You will have heard of bacteria, probably in the context of disease. There is a huge variety of bacteria, and most of them are harmless. They account for a large proportion of all single-celled creatures, and such creatures accounted for *all* life on Earth from the origin of life nearly 3900 million years ago until as recently as about 700 million years ago — multicelled creatures are a comparatively recent development.

A few single-cell creatures are shown in Figure 6.2 overleaf, where each cell is roughly a few hundredths of a millimetre across. A cell consists of a membrane that encloses liquid water plus other substances. It is in these substances in the cell that we discover the similarity between all organisms, substances that are common to all life on Earth, and that are essential for all life on Earth.

6.1.1 Chemical elements and compounds

The substances of interest are chemical compounds. To understand what is meant by a chemical compound you need to understand what is meant by a chemical element, and to understand this you need to know something about atoms.

For our purposes we can regard an **atom** as the smallest building block of a molecule, where a molecule is the smallest unit of a substance. Atoms are very small, about 10^{-10} m across. There are many sorts of atom, one sort being distinguished from another by its various properties, such as its mass, and the way in which it can interact with other atoms. A **chemical element** consists of a single type of atom. Over 100 chemical elements are known, and several of them are familiar in the everyday world, for example, hydrogen (H), helium (He), nitrogen (N), oxygen (O), neon (Ne), aluminium (Al), iron (Fe), silver (Ag), gold (Au), lead (Pb), uranium (U). These elements are denoted by the symbols in brackets after the element; those that are not obvious relate mainly to the Latin names of the element e.g. Fe comes from 'ferrum', meaning 'iron'. These letters are also used to denote a single atom of the element.

⬤ What letter denotes a single atom of hydrogen?

◯ H.

In an element the smallest unit might be a single atom. This is the case in neon for example. Thus a sample of neon consists of a collection of single atoms of neon. The smallest unit might also be small numbers of atoms bound together. Thus, in the oxygen in the air we breathe the smallest unit is two atoms of oxygen bound together. This is written as O_2. Thus a sample of oxygen consists of a collection of pairs of oxygen atoms.

In a **chemical compound** the smallest unit always contains more than one type of atom. For example, the smallest unit of water consists of two atoms of hydrogen and one atom of oxygen bound together. A sample of water then consists of a collection of these units.

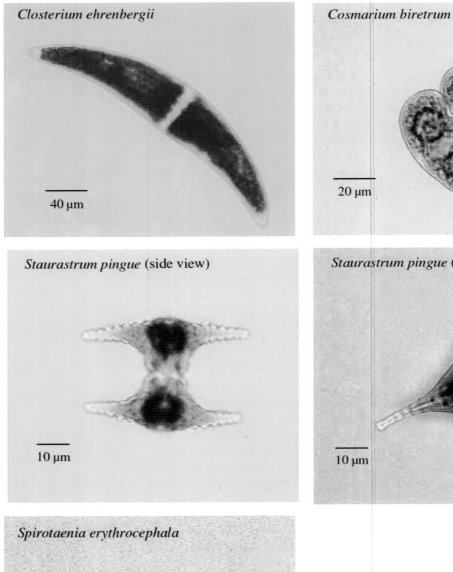

Closterium ehrenbergii

40 μm

Cosmarium biretrum

20 μm

Staurastrum pingue (side view)

10 μm

Staurastrum pingue (end view)

10 μm

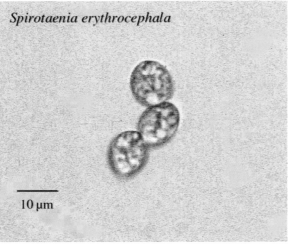

Spirotaenia erythrocephala

10 μm

Figure 6.2   A variety of single-celled organisms. In the bottom left case there is a colony of three single cells.

○ Guess how the single unit of water is denoted in terms of the symbols H and O.

○ The unit of water is written as H_2O. In fact, OH_2 makes as much sense, but convention dictates otherwise.

When the smallest unit in an element or in a compound consists of more than one atom it is called a **molecule**.

6.1.2 The chemical compounds of life, and their implications for searching for life elsewhere

When we look into the cell, at the fundamental chemicals of life, it is found that all life on Earth is based on huge molecules that are complex compounds of the chemical element carbon (C). Diamond is almost pure carbon, and carbon is present in carbon dioxide, CO_2. You will have heard of proteins and of DNA, and perhaps of RNA too. These are all huge and complex carbon compounds containing very many atoms per molecule, and they are all essential for the processes of all life on Earth. For example, DNA contains the information for making a new generation of organisms from the present one. It comes as no surprise to chemists that carbon is the basis of life — no other chemical element comes anywhere near carbon in its facility to form the large and complex compounds that are necessary for life.

So, in our search for potential habitats for life beyond the Earth we should restrict ourselves to places where huge, complex compounds of carbon can exist. The availability of carbon is no problem — carbon is a fairly common and widespread element. What really narrows the search is that *huge* carbon compounds can exist only under certain conditions of temperature.

○ Make an 'educated guess' as to what might happen to *huge* carbon compounds at sufficiently high temperatures.

○ They will break up.

Specifically, the huge carbon compounds that are the basis of life break up above about 150 °C, so we must confine our attention to places colder than this.

All life on Earth has some other requirements, but there is one more requirement that will be of great importance in aiding our search for life elsewhere. It is a chemical compound found in all cells, and it was referred to near the start of this section.

○ What substance does all life on Earth require?

○ All life on Earth, during at least some part of its life cycle, needs water.

What's more, the need is for *liquid* water. We must thus identify places where water exists, and where the temperature and pressure is such that the water is liquid.

○ At sea-level on the Earth, over what range of temperatures is water liquid?

○ Water is liquid between 0 °C and 100 °C at sea-level. Thus, if the temperature is lowered to 0 °C water freezes, and if it is raised to 100 °C it turns into vapour (gas) very rapidly i.e. it boils.

These boiling and freezing temperatures depend on atmospheric pressure. At sea-level on the Earth the average pressure is about 1000 millibars, the millibar being a unit of pressure that you might have seen on weather maps. At 1000 millibars the boiling temperature of water is 100 °C. On a mountain only 1000 metres high, the average pressure is reduced to about 900 millibars and the boiling temperature is consequently reduced to 97 °C. The boiling temperature is raised above 100 °C in a pressurized container. The freezing temperature is much less sensitive to pressure — for practical purposes we can regard the freezing temperature as 0 °C.

As the pressure is lowered below 900 millibars the boiling temperature of water continues to fall, and approaches 0 °C at a pressure of 6.1 millibars. Consequently, below 6.1 millibars, water cannot exist as a liquid, but only as a solid (ice) or a gas. For practical purposes, we can assume that if liquid water can exist, then complex carbon compounds can too.

To summarize: life on Earth can be described as carbon–liquid-water life, and in looking for life beyond the Earth, we therefore need to focus our attention on places where complex carbon compounds and liquid water could exist, conditions for the possible existence of liquid water being sufficient in practise. We then need to see if, in fact, these substances *do* exist, and whether life has emerged.

6.2   Potential habitats in the Solar System

In relation to carbon–water life, the type of potential extraterrestrial habitat that attracts almost exclusive attention is the surface regions of planets and their satellites, rather than interstellar clouds (such as the Coal Sack in Plate 1.14) and the surfaces of stars. In the case of stars it is the high temperatures that make them totally unsuitable for life. The reason for ignoring interstellar clouds is less obvious — it is because they are of such low density that it would be difficult to bring together enough atoms to build up huge carbon compounds in any quantity, and because the pressures are far too low for liquid water.

We can divide potential extraterrestrial habitats into two categories:

1   the planets and satellites in our Solar System

2   the planets and satellites in the planetary systems of other stars.

Activity 6.1   Where in the Solar System might we find life? (20 minutes)

On the basis of the information given in the table 'Basic data on the planets' in *IC*, make a list of each of the eight planets (not including the Earth), and state with reasons, whether each one is likely to be a potential extraterrestrial habitat. In some cases you might have to decide that insufficient information has been given to form any sort of judgement. ◄

From the comments on Activity 6.1 it is clear that, among the planets today, none (except the Earth) looks very promising as a potential habitat. This is borne out by further data on the planets. Only one planet has any realistic chance of being a potential habitat, and that is Mars. Among the planetary satellites there is a further candidate — Europa, which is one of the large satellites of Jupiter.

6.2.1   Mars

Mars is the next planet out from the Sun after the Earth (see the Solar System diagram in the introduction to Part 2 of *IC*). It is a rocky body, 3394 km in radius (about half that of the Earth), with a thin atmosphere of carbon dioxide, and surface temperatures that can reach 20 °C on a very good day. The average surface pressure, however, is close to the 6.1 millibar minimum for liquid water. Therefore, only in the very deepest chasms on Mars, where the pressure would be slightly higher, and even there only on the warmer days, could liquid water persist at the surface. However, there is no evidence of liquid water on the surface even at such favoured places, though there is water *ice* at the surface, for example in the polar caps (Plate 2.32), and there could well be permafrost just beneath the surface.

There is certainly no evidence for life at the martian surface. No tracts of vegetation have been seen from space, and the spacecraft that have landed on the surface have seen no lifeforms stalking the landscape. More significantly, the landers have discovered a total absence of the processes and chemical products of life in the martian sands, and though very little of the martian surface has been explored in this way it does seem unlikely that there is any life at the surface today. Missions planned for the next few years will provide further evidence.

If there is any life on Mars today then it would be deep under the surface, where the pressures are large and where heat from the planet's interior could keep the temperatures above 0 °C, and thus water could exist as a liquid. Evidence for such subsurface deposits of liquid water has been discovered recently in images taken by a spacecraft in orbit around Mars, imaginatively named Mars Global Surveyor. Figure 6.3 shows features that geologists believe could only have been carved by liquid water released from subsurface deposits, probably as the pressure of liquid water rose and burst through a permafrost layer. Though water-carved features were first seen in images of Mars acquired by the orbiting spacecraft Mariner 9 as long ago as 1971, these are in *old* terrain, indicating that those water flows occurred at least about 2000 million years ago (remember that the planets were formed 4600 million years ago — see Plate 2.1). The exciting thing about Figure 6.3 is that these features are in *young* terrain, indicating that liquid water is present not very far down. Activity 6.2 enables you to explore how we can establish ages for the various terrains of Mars.

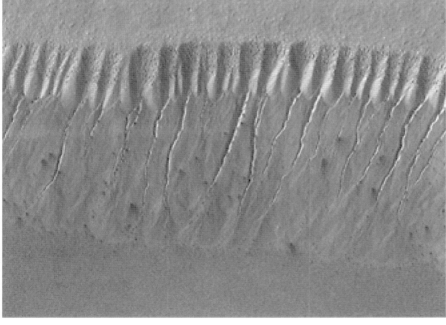

Figure 6.3 Recent features on Mars, thought to have been carved by liquid water bursting from underground. This landscape is only 2.7 km wide.

Activity 6.2 Dating the martian surface (20 minutes)

Study Plates 2.6 and 2.12 (and their captions), and hence explain how impact craters could be used to deduce that one terrain on the surface of Mars is older than another. Outline a simple demonstration of your own invention that would illustrate the principle. ◄

We thus have the possibility of life existing deep in Mars, just as on Earth we find life deep in the rocks, provided that liquid water can reach such places. But most astrobiologists (scientists whose research interests are in extraterrestrial life) consider life deep in Mars to be a remote possibility. By contrast they consider it much more likely that we will find evidence that there was life at the surface of Mars in the distant past, and that evidence for this will be found in the form of fossils. This opinion is based on the many water-carved features on ancient martian terrain, mentioned above, indicating that water was common as a liquid on the surface of Mars in that far-off time. This ancient terrain is at least about 2000 million years old, but the youngest of it is probably not older than about 3800 million years. With Mars 4600 million years old, the clement conditions could have lasted long enough for life to evolve, though probably not long enough for it to evolve beyond the single-cell stage.

Mars hit the headlines in 1996 after a NASA press conference was convened to announce the publication of a scientific paper claiming that biological microfossils had been discovered in a meteorite from Mars, known as ALH84001 (Section 2.5). This claim has been disputed, and the balance of opinion is that the tiny structures, and the accompanying chemical features of the meteorite, have a non-biological origin. Nevertheless, Mars has hardly been explored for fossils — we need to return to Mars to do a more thorough job, and it will take several decades of exploration by landers before this job will have been done. This task will start in 2003, when the European Space Agency mission *Mars Express* should go into orbit around Mars, and send the lander *Beagle 2* to the surface (this lander (Figure 6.4) is being masterminded within the OU's Planetary and Space Sciences Research Institute). A website with up-to-date information on martian meteorites which can be accessed via the S194 ROUTES gateway is:

  http://www.jpl.nasa.gov/snc/

Figure 6.4   The *Beagle 2* lander, destined to land on Mars in 2003.

6.2.2 Europa

Europa is one of the four large satellites of Jupiter, the others being Io, Ganymede, and Callisto. Comparison of the tables on the planets and their satellites at the back of *IC* shows these four satellites to be about the same size as Mercury, so they would be regarded as planets were they in their own orbits around the Sun rather than in orbit around Jupiter.

It is, however, the fact that Europa *is* in orbit around Jupiter that has led to the possibility of life being found there. This is because Jupiter causes a varying deformation of Europa. That a varying deformation can cause heating is exemplified by a squash ball, which gets heated when it is repeatedly deformed. Quite *why* Jupiter causes a varying deformation we shall come to in a moment, when you will also see that the consequent heating is called **tidal heating**. First, let's see why this heating is important to the prospect of finding life on Europa.

○ Examine the caption of Plate 2.22, and deduce why tidal heating is relevant to finding life on Europa.

○ Without tidal heating the liquid water at the surface of Europa would freeze.

With this component of heating, the liquid water exists, albeit under an outer shell of ice, a kilometre or so thick. Evidence for a widespread ocean includes close-up images of Europa, taken by the Galileo Orbiter, such as that in Figure 6.5. The icy surface here has been broken up into ice-rafts that floated apart until the water between them froze. In that widespread ocean it is possible that aquatic lifeforms exist today. We need to go to Europa, get through the ice, and have a look. Unfortunately there are, as yet, no firm plans to do so.

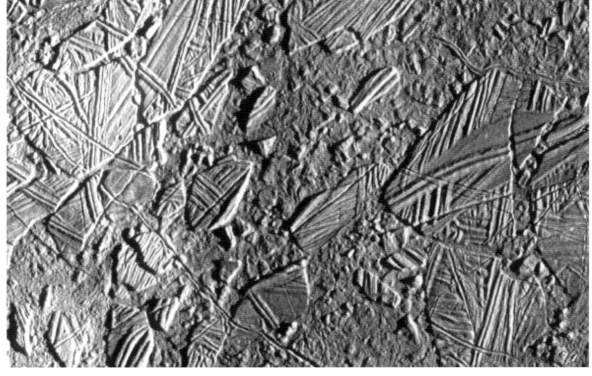

Figure 6.5   A Galileo Orbiter image of part of Europa. This region is about 40 km across.

To see how Jupiter causes the varying deformation of Europa that leads to the tidal heating, consider a very large, spongy ball falling towards Jupiter because of the gravitational attraction between the ball and Jupiter. Figure 6.6a shows the situation, where you can see that the ball really is *very* large! The ball can be notionally (not actually) divided into pieces of equal mass. We can do this in any way — Figure 6.6a shows two pieces of equal mass shown as red dots, one on the side nearest to Jupiter, and one on the side furthest from Jupiter. The force of gravity between two objects decreases as the distance between them increases.

So, on which of the two red dots will the force of Jupiter's gravity be greater?

It will be greater on the dot nearer to Jupiter.

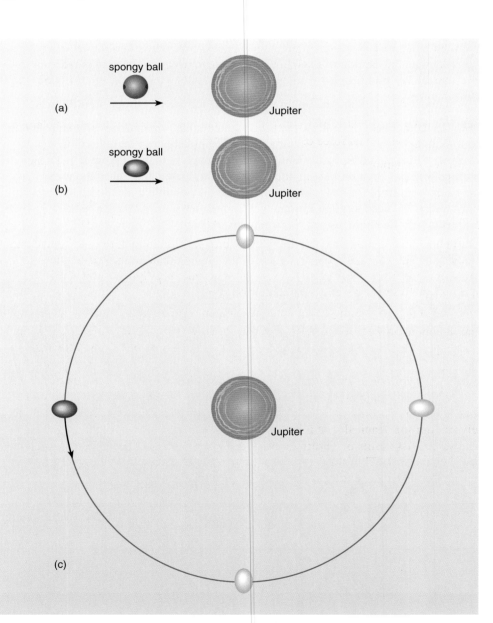

Figure 6.6 (a) A large, spongy ball falling towards Jupiter. (b) The distortion that would occur in the ball. (c) The ball in orbit around Jupiter, and keeping the same face towards Jupiter.

This will result in the two dots being pulled apart. For the ball as a whole we get a distortion as shown in Figure 6.6b, the shape resembling that of a rugby ball (or an American football). Because the distortion arises from a difference in gravitation force across the ball, it is called a *tidal distortion*, and the bulges are called *tidal bulges*.

In order to get the ball into orbit around Jupiter it would have to be launched sideways, just as in the case of a satellite in Earth orbit, as described in Section 2.3. Let's suppose that the ball always keeps the same face towards Jupiter, just as the Moon keeps the same face towards the Earth. In this case the tidal bulges will always lie on the line from the ball to Jupiter, as in Figure 6.6c. The distortion, from the point of view of the ball's interior, is fixed, so there will be no tidal heating.

To see how we get tidal heating, consider Europa itself. Figure 6.7a shows Europa in orbit around Jupiter, where we have *greatly* exaggerated the size of Europa, its tidal distortion, and the departure of its orbit from a circle. For the moment, suppose that the tidal bulges always lie on the line from Europa to Jupiter. You can see that we have shown a smaller tidal distortion the further Europa is from Jupiter. This is because not only does the gravitational force decrease with distance but so does the difference in gravitational force across an object.

If Europa were at an infinite distance from Jupiter, what would be the difference in the gravitational force of Jupiter across Europa?

The gravitational force due to Jupiter would be zero at all points on Europa, so the difference would also be zero.

This variation in tidal distortion as Europa goes around its orbit is rather like cycling the degree of distortion of a squash ball, and so we *do* now get tidal heating.

There is another contribution to the tidal heating because in fact, the tidal bulges do not stay on line, but behave as in Figure 6.7b. This means that the bulges move to and fro within the body of Europa as Europa goes around its elliptical orbit. This oscillating distortion gives rise to further heating.

You might wonder whether tidal heating can make other satellites of the giant planets into potential habitats. We need to concentrate on large satellites — small satellites cannot have their temperatures raised much by tidal heating or by any other form of heating. The reason is that the smaller a body the greater its surface area per unit of its mass, thus leading to more rapid loss of heat by radiation to space. In order from Jupiter, the large satellites are Io, Europa, Ganymede, and Callisto. Io is thus closer to Jupiter than is Europa, and it is heated even more strongly. It is heated too much, to give a highly volcanically active surface devoid of water — see Plates 2.26–2.28. Ganymede and Callisto are further away, and are not sufficiently heated for the outer ice shells to melt. The large satellites of Saturn, Uranus, and Neptune, are also insufficiently heated except at most to a very limited extent.

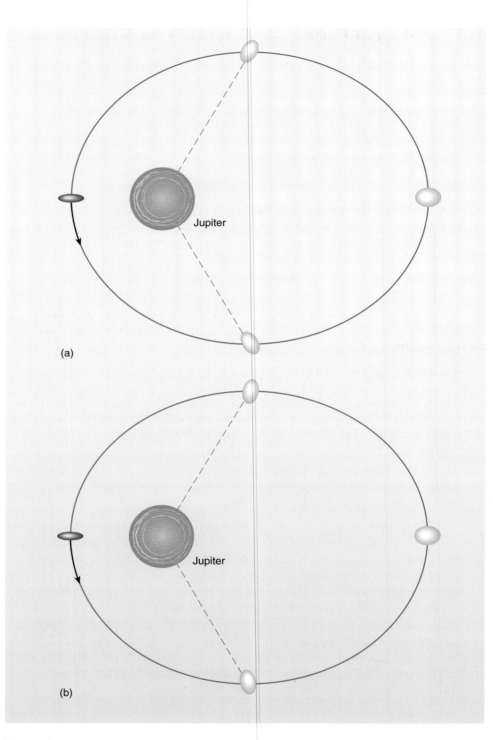

Figure 6.7 (a) Europa in orbit around Jupiter (the size of Europa, its tidal distortion, and the non-circularity of its orbit are exaggerated), with the tidal bulges lying on the line from Jupiter. (b) As (a), but with the tidal bulges failing to keep alignment.

6.3 Potential habitats beyond the Solar System

Beyond the Solar System we look to the planets and satellites of other stars as potential habitats. There is, however, a practical difficulty. Distances within the Solar System are relatively small, and so we have been able to send spacecraft to all the planets except the outermost one, Pluto, and our telescopes on Earth and in Earth-orbit have been able to establish a lot about the atmospheres and surfaces of the planets and their satellites. Once we look beyond the Solar System we encounter far larger distances to even the nearest stars.

⬤ How much further from us is the nearest star (Proxima Centauri) than Pluto?

◯ In Section 4.1 the distance to the nearest star (Proxima Centauri) is given as about 4×10^{13} km, and in Section 2.1 the distance to Pluto is given as 5.9×10^9 km. Therefore, the nearest star is about 4×10^{13} km/5.9×10^9 km times further away, which is nearly 10^4 times.

At such distances planets are too faint to be seen by our telescopes at present, particularly because their feeble light is drowned by the much greater light of their star, which would lie in nearly the same direction as any planet. It is rather like trying to detect the light of a glow-worm alongside a searchlight from a distance of many kilometres.

We therefore can only detect a planet through its effect on its star. One effect is on the motion of the star, as illustrated in a face-on view in Figure 6.8. The star goes around a tiny orbit — the motion of the star is greatly exaggerated in Figure 6.8. The star is readily seen and if the motion is sufficiently large or sufficiently rapid it can be detected by our telescopes. You can see that the star must move if you try the demonstrations in Activity 6.3.

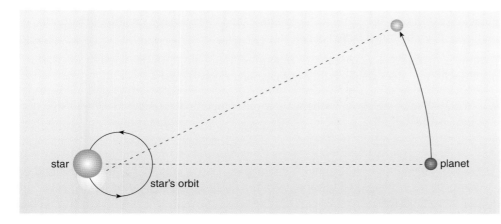

Figure 6.8 The orbital motion of a star due to a massive planet.

Activity 6.3 Motion of two bodies around each other (20 minutes)

In Activity 2.4 you whirled a light object (such as a cork) around on a piece of string. Repeat that demonstration now, and note that your hand (the 'star') hardly moves as the object goes around its circle. Now replace the object with something much heavier. Take care that no-one could be hit by the object as you whirl it, and that should you inadvertently let it go it will cause no damage to persons or property. When you whirl the heavy object you should find that your hand ('star') now has to go around a much larger orbit.

A similar large motion occurs when you face someone, hold hands at arms length, and whirl around. Neither of you will be able to turn on a fixed spot — you will both go around an orbit.

In these demonstrations gravity has been replaced by tension in string or arms, but the insight should be useful. ◀

So far stellar motion has been used to discover about forty other stars with planetary systems. These stars are all within about 200 ly of the Earth, so are in our back yard in terms of interstellar distances. The planets are all at least as massive as Saturn. Massive planets orbiting nearby stars are the easiest to detect. If there are any Earth-sized planets up there, then our technology should detect them in a few years. A detailed list of **exoplanetary systems** (as they are called) can be accessed via the S194 ROUTES gateway

http://cfa-www.harvard.edu/planets/catalog.html

At least a few percent of the nearby Sun-like stars have planetary systems. If this proportion is typical of the stars that can be seen at a dark site with the unaided eye, then at least several hundred of the visible stars will have planetary systems. Unfortunately, until we can obtain images of these planets and their satellites, we will be unable to tell if they are inhabited. It will not be until about 2010 at the earliest that we will have the instrumental capability to obtain such images. Then, if a planet is there, it will be imaged, though only as a single dot of light. So the question arises: 'how could we tell from such an image whether a planet is inhabited'.

6.3.1 Planetary spectra

The only way we could tell would be from the spectrum of the planet. The caption to Plate 1.4 shows what is meant by various sorts of spectra and illustrates one way of obtaining them. Consider first what we could learn from the continuous spectrum of a planet. We will take the Earth as an example, and consider the spectra of the Earth that have been obtained from space.

Examples of continuous spectra are shown in Figure 4.6. The spectrum of the Earth has broadly the same shape, but lies at far longer wavelengths.

● What is the name given to the wavelength range on the long wavelength side of the visible range?

○ Infrared.

The Earth's spectrum is at infrared wavelengths. This is emitted by the surface and the atmosphere — if we had infrared eyes the Earth's surface and the atmosphere would seem to glow!

● What do the wavelengths of emission from the Earth tell you about the Earth's average surface temperature, compared to those in Figure 4.6?

○ Comparison with Figure 4.6 shows that the Earth's surface must be a lot cooler than 2750 °C!

In fact, it can be inferred that the Earth's average surface temperature is about 15 °C. From other information in the spectrum (well beyond the scope of this course) the surface pressure can also be estimated, and we find, from our vantage point in space, that the pressure and temperature at the Earth's surface are suitable for water to be liquid. But can we tell that water is present? Yes we can, from the absorption features in the spectrum.

Plate 1.6 shows the absorption line spectrum of the Sun, where various substances in the Sun's atmosphere have depleted the light at certain wavelengths. As you learned in Section 4.2, from the wavelengths of these absorption lines we can determine the composition of the Sun's atmosphere, each line being associated with a particular substance. Likewise, the infrared spectrum of the Earth also shows absorption lines, and these are due to gases in the atmosphere. Some of these show that water is present as a gas (vapour) in the atmosphere, and it is possible to tell that there is enough of it so that there must be some condensed at the surface, where it would be predominantly in liquid form rather than as ice. We thus have the first requirement for life — liquid water — and it follows that the average surface temperature is low enough for huge carbon compounds to be stable. That carbon is present, is indicated by other absorption lines such as those due to carbon dioxide (CO_2) in the atmosphere.

We can thus establish that the conditions for carbon–water life exist on the Earth, but we have not yet shown that life is actually present. A strong indication is an absorption line due to ozone (O_3). Through chemical processes in the atmosphere this is derived from O_2, the oxygen that we breathe. O_2 does not have strong lines in the infrared spectrum. This does not matter — from the ozone line we can establish that oxygen as O_2 is a major constituent of the Earth's atmosphere. Oxygen is such a reactive substance that it would rapidly disappear from the atmosphere unless it was being regenerated at a very rapid rate. The best way we know of accomplishing this is through photosynthesis by green plants and other organisms.

Through **photosynthesis** an organism starts on the process of building its body tissues, which include huge, complex carbon compounds, from simple molecules, namely carbon dioxide and water. An energy source is required, and solar radiation is the one that most types of organisms use. Oxygen (O_2) is produced as a by-product by most types of photosynthesizing organisms. Without photosynthesis, the O_2 content of the Earth's atmosphere would be *far* lower. It is thus the ozone absorption feature that indicates strongly that the Earth is inhabited.

With planets around other stars we should be able to establish whether liquid water existed at the surface, and therefore whether the surface conditions were suitable for carbon–water life. If there was an ozone absorption feature we would be fairly confident that life was present. We would be confident if other absorption features were present, though space and time restrictions do not permit details to be given here.

Unfortunately, ozone could be below detectable limits even if life were present. This could happen under any one or more of three conditions.

1 Local lifeforms do not photosynthesize.
2 Local lifeforms do photosynthesize but oxygen is not released (there are some terrestrial organisms for which this is the case).
3 The rate of release of oxygen is so slow that the atmospheric abundance, in the face of removal processes, remains low.

However, even if there were no ozone line there could be other groups of absorption lines that would indicate the presence of life. Astrobiologists have identified such groups, but there is (again) no space here for details.

To conclude: we can say with some confidence that the next 20 years or so should resolve the issue of whether life is common in our neighbourhood of the cosmos.

6.4 Chapter summary

The essential points of Chapter 6 are as follows.

1 All lifeforms on Earth are based on complex carbon compounds, and require liquid water during at least part of their lifecycles.

2 In looking for extraterrestrial life we need to focus our attention on places where huge, complex carbon compounds and liquid water could exist, the possible existence of liquid water being sufficient in practise.

3 Within the Solar System, Mars and Europa are the best candidates for finding extraterrestrial life. At the surface of Mars today water can persist only as a solid, and there is no evidence for life on the martian surface. There might be life deep underground, where water could exist as a liquid. In the distant past, conditions on Mars were different, and liquid water could have persisted at the surface. Life might have evolved then, and so we might find fossils.

4 Europa is a rocky world overlain by an ocean of water and topped by a thin crust of ice. The water is maintained as a liquid with the aid of tidal heating. In the oceans there might be aquatic lifeforms.

5 Beyond the Solar System we look to planets of other stars. About 50 nearby stars are already known to have planetary systems. This is a few percent of the nearby Sun-like population, and this proportion can only grow. As yet we are unable to obtain images of the planets, but when we do, the spectra of the planets will enable us to investigate them for life.

6.5 End-of-chapter questions

Question 6.1 It has been suggested that, at temperatures too high for complex carbon compounds, life might be based on silicon. In a couple of sentences, make an 'educated guess' as to why chemists think this is unlikely. ◀

Question 6.2 As the Sun ages, its luminosity (power output) will gradually increase considerably. Explain why the Earth will eventually become uninhabitable. ◀

Question 6.3 If Europa were in its own orbit at its present distance from the Sun, rather than in orbit around Jupiter, why would we strike it off the list of possible habitats for life today? ◀

Question 6.4 If there were no life on Earth, explain one way in which the infrared spectrum of the Earth would be different. ◀

Question 6.5 If a spectrum was obtained of a planet considerably colder than the Earth, then how would the spectrum differ from that of the Earth? ◀

Galaxies

7

In this chapter you will get a glimpse of some of the most dramatic objects in the
Universe. You will also revisit some of the key ideas that you have met several times
already in the course — electromagnetic radiation, without which we would have no
astronomy, and angular size and scientific notation which are used not just in
astronomy but in many other areas of science.

7.1   The Milky Way galaxy

In Activity 3.3 you might have been able to see the Milky Way — a faint band of
light that arches across the sky. This faint light comes from millions of distant stars
and nebulae that make up a huge disc. Plate 3.2 shows an artist's impression of what
the disc would look like from the outside, and Plate 3.5a is a sort of sketch-map
showing where we are i.e. in one of the spiral arms, about two-thirds of the way out
from the centre. When we look out from Earth along the disc itself, we see the light
from many distant stars making up a faint band. Looking from the Earth's Southern
Hemisphere, the band appears thicker and brighter, which indicates that most of the
stars lie in that direction — we are looking towards a large bulge at the centre of the
disc. Plate 3.3 shows an image obtained from the Southern Hemisphere, arranged so
that the Milky Way runs across the picture with the brightest part in the centre. Plate
3.4 shows some whole-sky images (rather like drawing the whole world on one page
of an atlas), obtained at various wavelengths — note that they do not use a consistent
system of colour coding.

The Milky Way is a **galaxy** — a collection of about 10^{11} stars (a hundred thousand
million). Telescopes reveal that there are many other galaxies, scattered millions of
light years from the Milky Way. They vary in size and shape, but typically a galaxy
contains hundreds of millions of stars and measures tens of thousands of light years
across. Plate 3.1 shows one that is fairly similar to the Milky Way.

Have a look at all the parts of Plate 3.5 and its caption. This should remind you of
what you have learned about in Chapter 5. Notice the scale on Plate 3.5a, and notice,
too, that the stars and nebulae pictured in Plates 3.5b to e all lie quite near to our Sun
— at least, in comparison with the rest of the galaxy. The closest labelled object, the
Pleiades, is 410 light years from the Sun (about 4×10^{15} km), but that is 650 000
times further than the planet Pluto which orbits the Sun at about 6×10^9 km.

⬤ How many times bigger is the Milky Way galaxy than the Solar System?

◯ From Plate 3.2 caption, the radius of the Milky Way is about 50 000 light years.
   A light year is 9.46×10^{12} km, so 50 000 ly is $(50\,000 \times 9.46 \times 10^{12})$ km which is
   4.73×10^{17} km (i.e. almost 5×10^{17} km). Dividing 5×10^{17} km by 6×10^9 km we
   get 8.3333×10^7, i.e. about 8×10^7. In other words, the Milky Way is about
   80 million times bigger than the Solar System.

7.2 Other galaxies

Figure 7.1 was obtained with the Hubble Space Telescope, and shows several distant galaxies — anything that is not a small round blob (a star) is a galaxy! Plates 3.1 and 3.8 to 3.10 show just some of the many galaxies that have been observed, most of them far beyond the Milky Way. Notice the scales which are all labelled in arcmin or arcsec, reflecting the great distance of these galaxies — for a galaxy the size of the Milky Way to have an angular size of only a few arcmin, it must lie at a vast distance from us.

What is the relationship between the units arcsec, arcmin and degrees used to measure angles?

As you saw in Chapter 1, there are 60 arcmin in 1° and 60 arcsec in 1 arcmin and hence 3600 arcsec in 1°.

Suppose an astronomer observes two galaxies, one (galaxy A) with angular size 2 arcmin and another (B) with angular size 30 arcsec. If their overall appearance suggests that the two galaxies are very similar and hence likely to be similar in actual size, what can you say about the distances of the two galaxies?

The angular size of galaxy B is one-quarter that of galaxy A (2 arcmin is 120 arcsec) so B is more distant. Galaxy B will lie at about four times the distance of galaxy A.

Hubble Deep Field   HST · WFPC2
PRC96-01a · ST ScI OPO · January 15, 1996 · R. Williams (ST ScI), NASA

Figure 7.1   Some distant galaxies.

Notice that this line of reasoning gives astronomers another way of gauging distances. If two galaxies are thought to be the same size, then their relative distances can be found. But this is a big 'if': as you can see from the captions to Plates 3.8 to 3.10, galaxies come in a wide range of sizes.

○ As well as galaxies A and B (above) having different angular sizes, what other difference would be observed between them?

○ Galaxy A would appear brighter than galaxy B. Using the same line of reasoning that you saw in Chapter 4, galaxy B's distance is about 4 times that of A, so A's apparent brightness is about 4×4 (i.e. 16) times that of B.

7.2.1 Classifying galaxies

While each galaxy is different, they can be grouped into a few broad classes according to their appearance.

Activity 7.1 Galaxies (20 minutes)

Read the introduction to Part 3 of *IC*, and study Plates 3.8, 3.9 and 3.10 and their captions. Then list the characteristics of spiral, elliptical and irregular galaxies that distinguish them from one another. ◀

One key feature that characterizes the different classes of galaxy relates not only to the appearance of galaxies but also to the type of material they contain. Spiral and irregular galaxies have bright regions of active star formation, whereas ellipticals do not.

○ What does the lack of active star formation suggest about the content of elliptical galaxies? What is one key way in which our night sky would look different if we lived in an elliptical galaxy?

○ Elliptical galaxies have little or no ISM i.e. very little gas and dust between the stars. If we lived in such a galaxy we would still see stars, but there would be no nebulae such as the Orion, Trifid or Crab Nebulae.

7.2.2 Moving galaxies

By studying the light from galaxies, astronomers can study their stars, and compare and contrast them with our own Milky Way. They can also study the way galaxies move. One way to do this uses radio waves. The hydrogen gas that makes up most of the ISM in spiral and irregular galaxies gives out weak radio waves with a wavelength of 21 cm, which can be detected by tuning the receiver of a radio telescope to the appropriate wavelength (rather as you tune a radio set to pick up your chosen broadcast). However, if the hydrogen gas is moving away, the wavelength increases slightly, and if it is approaching the wavelength is shortened. You may have noticed a very similar effect as an emergency vehicle rushes past — when it is receding the sound of its siren has a lower pitch than when it is approaching. (For sound waves, a low pitch corresponds to a long wavelength.) This effect is called the **Doppler effect**, and it affects all types of waves, be they sound waves or electromagnetic waves such as radio or light. When light waves are affected, the lengthening is sometimes called a **redshift**, because the colours of visible light are shifted towards the red (long wavelength) end of the visible range.

By tuning their radio telescope to slightly different wavelengths close to 21 cm, astronomers can study the way that hydrogen gas is moving, and hence work out how galaxies move. Plate 3.12 shows the result of one such study carried out on a spiral galaxy known as M81 (Figure 7.2 shows a photograph of this galaxy) — and also shows yet another way in which images can be colour-coded. Here, blue indicates parts of the galaxy that are approaching and red those that are receding. Note that this galaxy is tilted with respect to our line-of-sight — we are not seeing it face-on.

Figure 7.2   The galaxy M81.

What does Plate 3.12 suggest about the motion of M81?

Taken as a whole, the shifts in wavelength show that the galaxy is rotating. The blue-coloured parts are swinging towards us, the green and yellow parts are moving across our field of view and the red-coloured parts are receding.

Similar investigations of other spiral galaxies reveal that they, too, are all rotating like giant wheels. Different techniques are used to study elliptical galaxies (they have little interstellar hydrogen), but they are found to have very little rotation.

7.2.3   Peculiar and active galaxies

Some galaxies have odd features that set them apart. Plates 3.13 and 3.15 show just two examples of so-called peculiar galaxies. Some galaxies are so odd that they cannot be placed in one of the usual classes. Plate 3.14 shows how a computer simulation has been used in an attempt to explain the strange shape of the Antenna Galaxy shown in Plate 3.13 — it seems to be the result of a collision between two spiral galaxies.

A small number of galaxies (a few per cent of the total) are known as active galaxies. An **active galaxy** is one that produces far more radiation than can be attributed to its stars and ISM alone. Plates 3.19 to 3.23 show examples of some active galaxies. The activity is thought to depend on the existence of a massive black hole at the galactic centre. Any detailed explanation of these exotic objects is beyond the scope of this short course, but spend a few minutes looking at these and studying their captions. Notice the very small angular sizes of some of the features, and their enormous distances and actual sizes — some are millions of light years across. Notice, too, the use of colour in the images to represent brightness of radiation: they do not all follow the same convention.

7.3 Clusters of galaxies

Galaxies are not just scattered randomly throughout space. By measuring distances to galaxies, astronomers can map the way they are distributed, and it turns out that they are clustered together so that some parts of space have a large number of galaxies while others have very few. The way galaxies group together is perhaps unexpected. Plates 3.29, 3.31 and 3.33 reveal that they tend to bunch together in long rope-like arrangements. Figure 7.3 shows the results of a more recent survey using infrared-sensitive telescopes, which shows an arrangement rather like a giant sponge.

The way that galaxies are distributed in space probably reflects the way that they were formed in the early Universe. To test their possible explanations, astronomers use computer simulations of the way galaxies might have formed. One of these is shown in Plate 3.37, which gives a fairly good imitation of the real distribution of galaxies.

7.3.1 Update

If you have internet access, you can view recent images of galaxies on the Hubble Space Telescope site, which can be accessed via the S194 ROUTES gateway:

> http://www.ast.cam.ac.uk

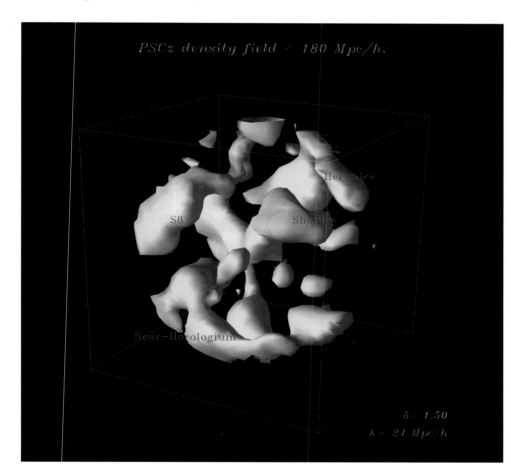

Figure 7.3 Three-dimensional contours of the galaxy distribution in a sphere of radius 600 million light years centred on the Milky Way. The large structures visible here are called 'superclusters'. This figure was constructed by E. Branchini, C. S. Frenk and L. Teodoro at Durham University from data in the PSCz survey. The survey is a collaboration involving researchers at Cambridge, Durham, Edinburgh, London (Imperial College) and Oxford Universities.

7.4 Chapter summary

The essential points of Chapter 7 are as follows.

1   The Sun is one of about 10^{11} stars that make up the Milky Way galaxy, a disc-shaped collection of stars measuring about 100 000 light years across.

2   Most galaxies can be classed as spiral, elliptical or irregular.

3   The distances of galaxies can sometimes be gauged from their angular sizes.

4   The Doppler effect can be used to measure the motions of galaxies.

5   Active galaxies emit far more electromagnetic radiation than can be accounted for by their stars and ISM alone.

6   Galaxies are grouped in space in rope-like arrangements.

7.5 End-of-chapter questions

Question 7.1   Figure 7.4 shows three galaxies. On the basis of its appearance, classify each as spiral, elliptical or irregular. ◀

Figure 7.4   Photographs of galaxies for Question 7.1.

(a)

(b)

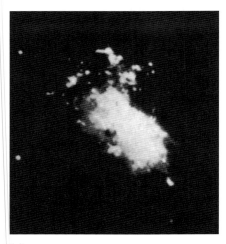

(c)

Question 7.2   List the following in increasing order of size (actual size not angular size). The Milky Way (Plate 3.2); the feature known as the Great Wall (Plate 3.33); the Solar System; the active galaxy Centaurus A (Plate 3.19); the star cluster M13 (Plate 3.6b). ◀

Question 7.3   Suppose that there are two very similar galaxies, one lying three times further from the Earth than the other. Describe as fully as possible the ways in which the galaxies will appear different when viewed from the Earth. ◀

8 The Universe

We end by considering the whole Universe, starting with the movement of galaxies, which gives us a clue as to how the Universe began.

8.1 The expanding Universe

As well as mapping galaxies in space, astronomers can also study the way that whole galaxies move. To do this, they use spectral lines. We briefly mentioned stellar spectral lines in Chapter 4. They are the characteristic colours (or wavelengths) in the light from a star (or galaxy) that depend on the substances present (see Plates 1.4 to 1.6). Just like the 21 cm radio spectral line is used to reveal the rotation of spiral galaxies, other spectral lines are seen at different wavelengths if their source is moving.

🔵 If the pattern of lines in a galaxy's spectrum is shifted to longer wavelengths, what can be deduced about the galaxy's motion?

⚪ The galaxy is receding from us. As you saw in Chapter 7, motion away from the observer gives rise to an increase in wavelength i.e. a redshift.

Measurements of redshifts of distant galaxies lead to the somewhat surprising result that they are all moving away from us — and the more distant they are, the faster they are moving. The Universe is expanding and it seems as though the galaxies are all part of a huge explosion. Looking at the speeds and distances, astronomers can work out that the explosion took place about 15 billion years ago. (To see how this can be estimated, imagine running a video clip of an explosion backwards until all the pieces come back together.) This explosion is known as the **Big Bang** — the event that is thought to have started the Universe.

The observation that galaxies are all moving away from us seems to imply that we occupy a privileged position at the centre of the Universe. However, a simple experiment shows this not to be the case.

Activity 8.1 The expanding Universe (20 minutes)

For this activity you need a wide rubber band, a pen and a ruler.

Draw some dots on the rubber band, a few cm apart (no need to be exact). These represent galaxies at one moment in the history of the Universe.

Choose one dot to be the Milky Way. Measure the distance from 'the Milky Way' to each other 'galaxy'.

Now stretch the rubber band as in Figure 8.1. The dots now represent galaxies at some later time in the history of the Universe. Hold the rubber band next to the ruler and roughly measure the distance of each galaxy from the 'Milky Way'. You will find that the galaxies that were furthest away to start with have moved through the greatest distance — in other words, they have moved fastest.

Repeat with a different galaxy representing the Milky Way. You will get the same result. ◀

Activity 8.1 shows that, whichever galaxy we lived in, we would always see the other galaxies moving away. You can use a balloon to demonstrate the same thing, as shown in Plate 3.35. No galaxy can be said to lie at the centre of the Universe — the Universe has no centre.

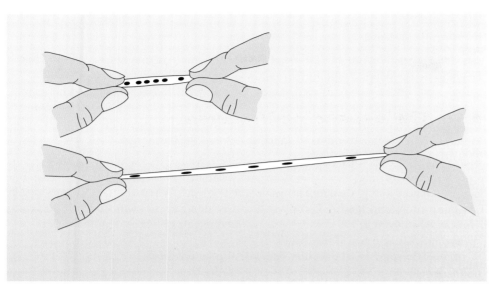

Figure 8.1 Modelling galaxies in an expanding universe.

8.2 Distance and redshift

It was the American astronomer Edwin Hubble (who also devised the classification scheme of the galaxies) who discovered the expansion of the Universe. In the 1920s he measured the redshifts of several galaxies and also measured their distances. From the redshifts he deduced that the galaxies were receding and was also able to work out their speeds. To his surprise, he found that there was a simple connection between the speeds and the distances. The more distant a galaxy, the faster it is receding; for example, if one galaxy lies at twice the distance of another, it also has twice the recession speed. This led Hubble to the mind-blowing conclusion that the Universe must be expanding, since the observed relationship between distance and recession speed is just as you found in Activity 8.1.

The relationship between distance and recession speed is known as **Hubble's law**, and provides astronomers with another method of gauging distances. A galaxy's recession speed can be calculated from measurements of its spectrum; the greater the redshift, the greater the speed. Knowing the speed, it is then possible to deduce the distance. Plate 3.11 shows some of Hubble's images of distant galaxies (labelled with the constellations in which they are seen), together with his measurements of their distances and recession speeds.

 Use the measurements given in Plate 3.11 for the galaxies in Virgo, Ursa Major, and Hydra to show that recession speed and distance do indeed increase more-or-less 'in step' with one another.

The Ursa Major galaxy's distance is 12.8 times that of the Virgo galaxy, and its recession speed is 12.5 times that of the Virgo galaxy. The Hydra galaxy's distance is 51 times that of the Virgo galaxy, and its recession speed is also 51 times that of the Virgo galaxy. (The agreement is not exact because the speeds and, particularly, the distances are difficult to measure precisely.)

Establishing the exact connection between distance and recession speed is an on-going challenge for astronomers, since it requires accurate and reliable measurements of distances to very distant galaxies which are difficult to achieve in practice.

○ Outline two ways, that you have met in this course, that astronomers can use to measure distances.

○ One way is to apply the 'far means faint' idea that you met in Chapter 4. If two objects are identical, the further one will appear fainter by an amount that depends on the square of its distance relative to the closer object. Another is to use angular sizes as indicated in Chapters 1 and 7. If two identical objects are at different distances, the angular size of the more distant one will be smaller by an amount that depends on its distance relative to the closer one.

○ Suggest why there will be problems applying these methods to distant galaxies.

○ Both methods rely on comparing identical objects. When observing a very distant galaxy, it is very hard to know whether it is identical (or even similar) to a nearby one. Also, even if it is possible to say that one galaxy is, say, ten times more distant than another, if the distance of the closer galaxy is not known exactly, then the distance to the further one will also be uncertain.

Using either apparent brightness or angular size to deduce distance involves making assumptions about the nature of very distant objects, which may or may not be reliable — but astronomers have to use what's available, and most methods for finding distance essentially boil down to using either size or brightness. In the decades since Hubble did his work, the details of the methods of distance measurements, the assumptions that underlie them, the types of objects studied and the instruments used in the observations, have been developed and refined, but astronomical distance measurement is still an area fraught with difficulty.

 Because of the difficulty in devising reliable distance measurements, astronomers tend to quote redshifts (or recession speeds) rather than distances when they are considering very distant galaxies, since these quantities are easy to work out directly from spectral lines. Plate 3.32 is a case in point.

Activity 8.2 Speed and distance (15 minutes)

Recent measurements indicate that, to have a recession speed of 1000 km per second a galaxy must lie at about 46 million light years from Earth.

 Use Hubble's law in conjunction with this information to work out the distance scale of Plate 3.32 and thus to deduce the distance of the furthest galaxies measured in the survey shown.

Compare Hubble's figures from Plate 3.11 with the more recent measurements of speed and distance. Comment on the difference. ◄

8.3 The very early Universe

By studying very distant galaxies and other objects, we are in fact looking back to the early history of the Universe. To see how this comes about, think about what we are actually seeing when our telescopes observe a distant object.

○ Think of a galaxy at a distance of 300 million light years. How long will light from this galaxy take to reach Earth? For this light to be entering our telescopes today, how long ago must it have left its source?

○ Light will take 300 million years to reach Earth. To be detected today, it must have set off from the galaxy 300 million years ago.

We are therefore seeing the galaxy not as it is now, but as it was 300 million years ago. In the intervening time, the galaxy might have changed — it might now be giving out more light, or less, but there is no way we could know that without waiting for the more recently-emitted light to reach Earth. It is a bit like the days when letters could only be carried as fast as people or horses could travel — there were no telephones or email. At best, a letter could only tell you the latest news from the time it was written, which might have been several days before the letter arrived. You would have no way of knowing what might have happened to the writer since the letter was posted.

A time of 300 million years is fairly short compared with the 15 billion years for which the Universe has existed. Even so, the time for which the light has been *en route* is about one-fiftieth of the present age of the Universe, so by looking at this distant galaxy, we are studying an object that was present in the Universe when it was 98% of its present age.

To get a glimpse of objects typical of the Universe when it was much younger, we need to look at even more distant objects. Some of the most distant objects yet discovered are the **quasars**. Plate 3.23 shows the nearest known quasar and its caption gives some information about these exotic objects.

○ The caption to Plate 3.23 mentions a quasar lying at a distance of 10 000 million light years. How old was the Universe when the light we are now seeing left this quasar?

○ The light must have been emitted 10 000 million (10 billion) years ago. As the Universe is now 15 billion years old, it must have then been just 5 billion years old — one-third of its present age.

By observing quasars, then, we are studying objects that were present in a much younger universe than the one we inhabit today. Since we *only* observe quasars at great distances, it seems reasonable to deduce that they existed only in the past. It may be that some of the galaxies that today give out only 'normal' starlight, were once quasars giving out copious amounts of light and other electromagnetic radiation. Quasars might be a type of active galaxy, powered by a massive black hole (Section 7.2).

8.3.1 Afterglow of the Big Bang

There is another key piece of evidence for the idea of a Big Bang at the start of the Universe. Telescopes sensitive to microwave radiation pick up a weak signal from all over the sky, which does not seem to be coming from any objects in particular (Plates 3.38 and 3.39). This radiation is typical of that which would be given out by an extremely cold object with a temperature of $-270\,°C$. It turns out that this microwave 'background radiation' is just what would be expected if the Universe had started off as a hot dense fireball and expanded to its present state, thus cooling the radiation. Plates 3.40 and 3.41 show whole-sky maps of this radiation, colour-coded to bring out some very small variations in its brightness. These tiny variations can be interpreted as 'lumps' in the very early Universe which eventually formed galaxies. Small wonder that, when these maps were first published in the early 1990s, they made front page news — in a sense, they are a picture of the dawn of the Universe.

8.4 Chapter summary

The essential points of Chapter 8 are as follows.

1 The motion of distant galaxies suggests that the Universe began with a Big Bang.

2 Hubble's law provides astronomers with a means of gauging distances to very distant galaxies and quasars.

3 Microwave background radiation provides evidence for the Big Bang and reveals the origins of galaxies.

8.5 End-of-chapter questions

Question 8.1   A certain galaxy is found, from the redshift of its spectrum, to be receding at 9600 km per second. Using information from this chapter, calculate the distance to the galaxy in light years. ◀

Question 8.2   Suppose that you are talking to a friend who has heard of the Big Bang but reckons it is 'only a theory, with no basis in fact'. What would you say in explanation? ◀

Summing up

9.1 End-of-course questions

Each of these questions covers material from more than one chapter. They will not only help you further develop your understanding of the course, they will also help you prepare for the End of Course Assessment, which includes questions that also cover more than one chapter.

Question 9.1 How much bigger is the radius of the Sun (1.4 million km) than the thickness of its photosphere (500 km)? Express your answer both in scientific and ordinary notation. ◄

Question 9.2 In the early seventeenth century, the astronomer Galileo Galilei (1564–1642) observed Venus through a telescope. He found that, like the Moon, it went through phases from crescent to full, and also that as its phase changed so did its angular size as shown in Figure 9.1.

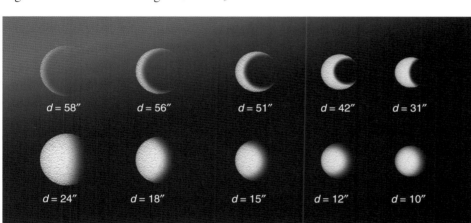

d = 58″ d = 56″ d = 51″ d = 42″ d = 31″

d = 24″ d = 18″ d = 15″ d = 12″ d = 10″

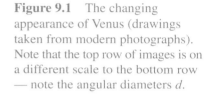

Figure 9.1 The changing appearance of Venus (drawings taken from modern photographs). Note that the top row of images is on a different scale to the bottom row — note the angular diameters *d*.

With the aid of a sketch, explain how the relative motion of Earth and Venus around the Sun can account for the ways that the appearance of Venus changes. ◄

Question 9.3 The planet Venus is sometimes referred to as the 'morning star' or 'evening star'. By referring to the diagram you drew for Question 9.2, explain why Venus can only be observed close to sunrise or sunset (and never at midnight) and say roughly whereabouts in the sky you would expect to see it. ◄

Question 9.4 In searching for exoplanets which may support life, astronomers are looking for evidence of rocky planets orbiting other stars. Explain why planets containing a large proportion of icy materials are unlikely to provide conditions suitable for the evolution of living organisms. ◄

Question 9.5 Some galaxies are called 'starburst galaxies' because they seem to be undergoing an enormous burst of star formation. Such galaxies are powerful sources of infrared radiation. (Plates 3.17 and 3.18 show starburst galaxies.) Write a few sentences to describe what must be happening in the ISM of such galaxies, and explain why this gives rise to infrared emission. ◄

Question 9.6 Galaxies and quasars with large redshifts do not necessarily appear redder than those that are closer to Earth. Suggest a reason for this. ◄

Question 9.7   A friend has just been to a talk on astronomy, and says

'I'm confused. The lecturer told us that the individual stars we can see making up constellations are relatively close and are all in our Milky Way galaxy. Then they talked about other galaxies which were much further away and contained billions of stars. But then they talked about other galaxies being in constellations like Cygnus. That doesn't seem to make sense.'

What would you say to your friend to sort out their confusion? ◄

Question 9.8   The background radiation is brightest at a wavelength of about 1 mm (i.e. it consists mainly of microwaves). In the distant future, when the Universe has expanded and cooled considerably, how will the background radiation differ from that which is observed today? ◄

Question 9.9   An astronomer observes two elliptical galaxies, whose overall shape and colour indicate that they are very similar. One has an angular size of 2 arcmin and a recession speed of 1320 km per second. The other has an angular size of 30 arcsec and appears to be a bit less than one-fifteenth as bright as the other. Deduce the distance to the fainter galaxy. Express your answer in light years and in metres. ◄

9.2   The end of the course: what next?

Now that you have completed this course you have experienced an overview of most areas of astronomy. We hope you have enjoyed it and found it interesting. In this short course, we have had to leave many questions unanswered, for example:

•   Will the Universe keep expanding for ever?

•   What fuels the vast power output of active galaxies?

•   How do some galaxies acquire a spiral structure?

•   Why do some stars explode when they have exhausted their nuclear fuel?

•   What are the nuclear reactions that take place inside stars?

•   Why are the giant planets so similar to one another yet so different from the terrestrial planets?

•   How did the Earth acquire its life-supporting atmosphere?

If you are intrigued by such questions, then you would probably like to learn more about astronomy and perhaps some other areas of science. There are several Open University courses that might interest you. Details can be found in the Study Guide.

Good luck in your future studies.

Questions: answers and comments

Our comments are in curly brackets { }. These are not expected to have been in your answers.

Question 1.1   The range is from about 1 m down to a bit less than 0.001 m. (The short end of the range lies just over three marks to the left of the 1 m mark i.e. a bit shorter than 0.001 m.)

Question 1.2   Plate 1.7a (X-rays, i.e. shortest wavelength); Plate 1.8 (ultraviolet); Plate 1.7e (whole visible spectrum); Plates 1.7d and 1.9 (red end of visible spectrum); Plate 1.7c (infrared); Plate 1.7b (radio, i.e. longest wavelength).

Question 1.3   Conventional fuels could only maintain the Sun's output of light and heat for a few thousand years which is not nearly long enough to sustain the evolution of life on Earth over the millions of years deduced from fossil records. Nuclear reactions produce *much* more energy output for a given amount of fuel, enabling the Sun to produce a steady output over thousands of millions of years.

Question 1.4   There are two methods for doing this question.

METHOD 1

The expression given

  actual size = (angular size in degrees × distance) ÷ 57

can be rewritten as

  diameter of Sun
  = (angular size of Sun in degrees × distance of Sun) ÷ 57.

The angular size of the Sun is about the same as that of the Moon, i.e. 0.5°. So

  diameter of Sun
  = (0.5 × 150 million km) ÷ 57 = 1.32 million km.

METHOD 2

The Sun's diameter is about 400 times the diameter of the Moon. Therefore, if the Moon is 3476 km in diameter then the Sun must have a diameter of about

  400 × 3476 km = 1.39 million km.

{This is not as accurate as in Method 1, because Chapter 1 says that the diameter of the Sun is *about* 400 times the diameter of the Moon.}

Question 1.5   (a) There are 60 arcmin in one degree (1°), so the Sun's angular size is 30 arcmin. Angular size of sunspot is

  30 arcmin ÷ 20 = 1.5 arcmin.

(b) 1 arcmin is 60 arcsec, so 1.5 arcmin = 90 arcsec.

Question 2.1   150 million km = 150 000 000 km

= 150 000 000 000 m = $1.5 \times 100\,000\,000\,000$ m
= 1.5×10^{11} m.

Question 2.2   Terrestrial planets are similar in size to the Earth and much smaller than the giant planets and they lie much closer to the Sun than the giants. They have at most two natural satellites each and no ring systems. They are composed mainly of rocky materials, whereas the giants also contain icy materials and have envelopes of hydrogen and helium.

Question 2.3   Comets must have formed in the outer parts of the Solar System. In order for icy materials to condense into solid grains and come together to form a comet, low temperatures would be required, and such temperatures would only prevail far from the Sun.

Question 2.4   Geostationary satellites are placed in orbits such that their motion just keeps pace with the surface of the Earth rotating beneath them. Like all satellites, they are launched 'sideways' and gravity keeps them in orbit.

Question 2.5   You might mention the need to set up large teams of people, possibly involving agreements which have to be negotiated between different countries. Then you could talk about the detailed background research, and the planning, design and testing of instruments which need to be very thorough because there is no second chance to get things right once the mission is launched.

Question 2.6   The flight path would need to be computed very accurately in order not to miss the target. The gravity between the asteroid and space probe would be weak, so it would be difficult to maintain orbital motion. {The space probe had to be slowed to a very low speed so that it would go into orbit and not drift off into space.}

Question 2.7   {The caption to Plate 2.5 lists several features that distinguish an impact crater from a volcanic crater.}

Question 3.1   Because Orion is in the southerly sky at midnight on New Year's Day, it must be in the opposite direction to the Sun (Figure 3.9). Therefore, six months later, when the Earth is on the other side of the Sun, Orion will be in roughly the same direction in the sky as the Sun. {It will therefore be invisible.} See Figure 3.9.

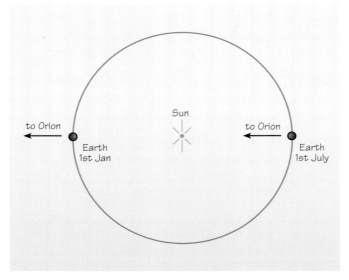

Figure 3.9   For Question 3.1.

Question 3.2   See Figure 3.10.

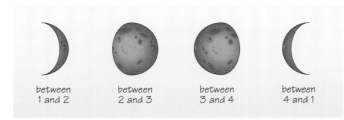

Figure 3.10   For Question 3.2.

{When the Moon is less than half-full it is called a crescent. When it is between half-full and full it is called gibbous. The Moon is said to be 'young' between new and first quarter, and 'old' between third quarter and new. It is said to be waxing between new and full, and waning between full and new.}

Question 3.3   The Moon has a far side in the sense that there is a side that does not face the Earth. It does *not* have a dark side: Figure 3.3a shows that every region of the Moon is in sunlight at some time in the lunar orbit.

Question 3.4   Plate 1.14 shows that there is a band of stars crossing the region of the Southern Cross. At lower resolution these stars would blend together and would appear like the Milky Way. Therefore a reasonable guess is that the Milky Way consists of a huge number of stars. {This is correct, as you can see if you have binoculars or a telescope and examine the Milky Way in your skies.}

Question 4.1   Three of the stars are bluish–white so they must have similar temperatures, but the one nearest the top of the picture is orange so it must be quite a bit cooler. Of the three bluish stars, the one nearest the bottom of the picture is brightest so it is probably the nearest, while the one on the right is faintest so it is probably the most distant. {Notice that we have said 'probably' because we cannot be sure that all these three stars are of similar size as well as having similar temperatures. Notice, too, that we have said nothing about the distance of the reddish star because we can only compare like with like.}

Question 4.2   By extending Table 4.2 upwards for two rows, you can see that 0.000 001 metres (one millionth of a metre) is 10^{-6} metres. Extending the table by another six rows to a millionth of a millionth we get 0.000 000 000 001, which is 10^{-12} in scientific notation.

Question 5.1   Dense cloud; protostar; main sequence star; red giant; white dwarf + planetary nebula.

Question 5.2   The Trifid Nebula is a site of star formation, where molecular cloud fragments collapse to form protostars and then young stars whose radiation heats the surrounding gas causing it to glow.

The Helix Nebula is a planetary nebula i.e. material ejected from the outer parts of a star after it has exhausted its main fuel supply and become a red giant. The remaining central core of the star becomes a white dwarf.

The Crab Nebula is a supernova remnant; the material ejected when a star over eight times the mass of the Sun was shattered in a tremendous explosion after exhausting its nuclear fuel. In this case the remaining central core of the star becomes a pulsar while another possibility would have been the formation of a black hole.

Question 6.1   To quote Section 6.1 'no other chemical element comes anywhere near carbon in its ability to form (complex) compounds'. It is believed that life must be based on huge, complex chemical compounds, and silicon is unlikely to form sufficiently huge, complex compounds.

Question 6.2   A considerable increase in solar luminosity will cause an increase in the Earth's surface temperature to the point where it is too hot for liquid water and for huge, complex carbon compounds. The Earth will then be uninhabitable. {The surface of Mars might have a period of being inhabitable. This is because a warmer surface will lead to gases, notably carbon dioxide, being released from the surface thus increasing the atmospheric pressure to the point where water can exist as a liquid.}

Question 6.3   If Europa no longer orbited Jupiter then it would no longer be tidally heated, and so its oceans would freeze. {It would then resemble many of the other satellites of the outer planets.}

Question 6.4   With no life on Earth there would be no photosynthesis, hence little oxygen, hence little ozone, and so the ozone absorption line would, at most, be very weak. {There would be other changes too, beyond the scope of this course.}

Question 6.5   {There are at least three changes that you might have thought of, based on the information given in this course.}

1   The peak in the spectrum would be at longer wavelengths.

2   Life would be unlikely on a cold world, so there would be no ozone absorption line.

3   A cold atmosphere would contain little water vapour, so water absorption lines would be weak.

Question 7.1   Galaxy (a) is elliptical. It has a smooth oval shape and no sign of spiral arms or a central bulge.

Galaxy (b) is spiral. It has a central bright concentration of light (the bulge) and clear spiral arms.

Galaxy (c) is irregular. It has an irregular shape and irregular distribution of light.

Question 7.2   Smallest is the Solar System, which is very much less than 1 ly across. Next M13, which lies within the Milky Way and is about 150 ly across. Then comes the Milky Way (about 100 000 ly across), then Centaurus A (2.5 million ly) and finally the Great Wall of galaxies which is about 200 million ly long.

Question 7.3   The more distant galaxy will have a smaller angular size and will also appear fainter. Its angular size will be about one-third that of its nearer counterpart, and its apparent brightness will be one-ninth. (It is also possible that the two galaxies will be seen in different orientations e.g. either face-on or obliquely, but one cannot be definite about that.)

Question 8.1   A galaxy with a recession speed of 1000 km per second has a distance of about 46 million light years (see Comment on Activity 8.2). Using Hubble's law, we can deduce that a speed of 9600 km per second puts the galaxy at a distance of 9.6×46 million light years i.e. 441.6 million light years (which is near enough 440 million).

Question 8.2   You could describe two key observations that support the idea of the Big Bang. First: galaxies are observed to be moving apart from one another (you might go on to say something about redshift, making the comparison with the sounds from receding vehicles). Second, microwave-sensitive telescopes pick up faint radiation that is best interpreted as the 'afterglow' of a hot explosion that involved the whole Universe.

Question 9.1   1.4 million km is 1.4×10^6 km, so the ratio is $1.4 \times 10^6 \div 500$ i.e. 2.8×10^3 or 2800. {Chapters 1 and 2}

Question 9.2 Figure 9.2 shows that, when Venus and Earth are on the same side of the Sun, only a small part of the illuminated surface of Venus will be visible, whereas when they are on opposite sides Venus will appear 'full'. The angular size of Venus, as measured from Earth, is greatest when it is close to the Earth and smallest when it is furthest away, and so the 'crescent' phases will correspond to a large angular size and the 'full' phase will be seen when the angular size is smallest. {Chapters 1, 2 and 3}

Question 9.3 Observed from Earth, Venus always lies in a similar direction to the Sun so always appears close to the Sun in the sky. To appear in the midnight sky, Venus would need to lie in the opposite direction to the Sun, and this never occurs (see Figure 9.2). As Venus always appears close to the Sun, it will be seen either in the western sky shortly after sunset, or in the eastern sky shortly before sunrise. {Chapters 2 and 3}

Question 9.4 It is thought that liquid water is one of the essential requirements for the formation and evolution of living organisms. Planets containing a large proportion of icy material would form only at quite large distances from their parent stars, where temperatures are low enough to allow icy materials to form solid grains. If temperatures are so low, the planet will probably be too cold for water to be present in liquid form and hence unable to sustain living organisms. {Chapters 2 and 6}

Question 9.5 Molecular clouds in the ISM must be colliding, fragmenting and collapsing under their own gravity to form protostars and, eventually, stars. This gives rise to strong infrared radiation because the fragments heat up as they collapse and hence emit the infrared radiation characteristic of warm objects. Also, radiation (mainly visible and ultraviolet) from newly-formed stars will heat the surrounding gas and dust so that it, too, emits in the infrared. {Chapters 4 and 5}

Question 9.6 If galaxies and quasars emit a lot of ultraviolet radiation, then the effect of the redshift will be to bring this radiation into the visible part of the spectrum. If the light received contains more blue than red, the galaxy or quasar will appear bluish. {Chapters 4, 7 and 8}

Question 9.7 You would need to explain that constellations are just apparent groupings of stars that appear in a similar direction when viewed from Earth but are not necessarily close to one another. When astronomers say that something is 'in' a constellation they mean that it is seen in that part of the sky, and that does not necessarily mean it is physically close to any of the stars. (You might go on to reassure your friend that what they remember being been told about nearby stars and distant galaxies is quite right.) {Chapters 4 and 7}

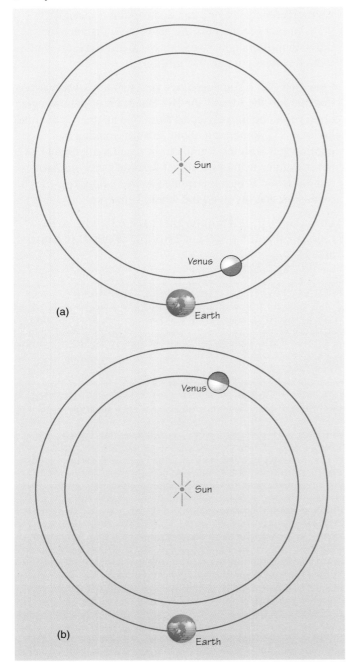

Figure 9.2 Explaining the changing appearance of Venus: (a) crescent phase, large angular size; (b) full phase, small angular size.

Question 9.8 The brightness will peak at a longer wavelength. Over time, it will move from the microwave to the radio part of the spectrum. This is because the radiation depends on the temperature at which it is emitted, and a cooler object — a cooler Universe — will produce radiation at longer wavelengths. {Another way to think of this is to think of the wavelength of the radiation that pervades the Universe being 'stretched' as space itself expands.} {Chapters 4 and 8}

Question 9.9 A recession speed of 1320 km per second for the brighter galaxy corresponds to a distance of 1.320×46 million light years i.e. 60.72 million light years (near enough 61 million). {Chapter 8}

Comparing the angular sizes indicates that the fainter one lies at about four times the distance (its angular size is one-quarter that of the brighter galaxy). {Chapters 1 and 7}

If this were the case, we would expect it to appear about one-sixteenth as bright — so 'a bit less than one-fifteenth as bright' is as we would expect. Its distance would therefore be 4×61 million light years i.e. 244 million light years. {Chapter 4}

1 light year is 9.46×10^{12} km, so the 244 million light years is $244 \times 10^6 \times 9.46 \times 10^{12}$ km i.e. 2.308×10^{21} km (near enough 2.3×10^{21} km). {Chapter 4}

Comments on activities

Activity 1.1 Figure 1.8 shows our summary description of the Sun based on Sections 1.1 and 1.2 of Chapter 1. Yours may be presented in a different way but should include similar information.

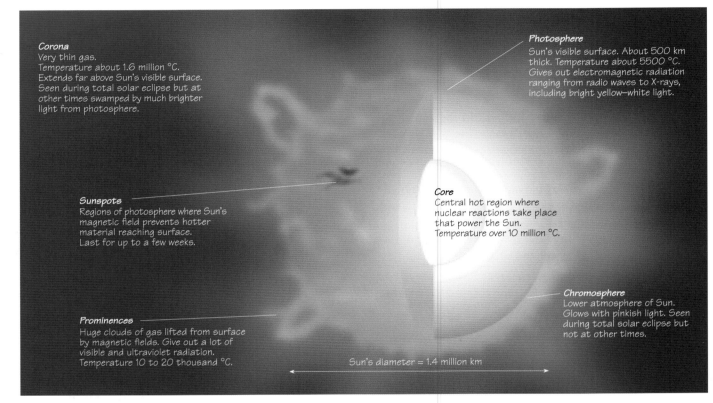

Corona
Very thin gas.
Temperature about 1.6 million °C.
Extends far above Sun's visible surface.
Seen during total solar eclipse but at other times swamped by much brighter light from photosphere.

Photosphere
Sun's visible surface. About 500 km thick. Temperature about 5500 °C.
Gives out electromagnetic radiation ranging from radio waves to X-rays, including bright yellow–white light.

Sunspots
Regions of photosphere where Sun's magnetic field prevents hotter material reaching surface.
Last for up to a few weeks.

Core
Central hot region where nuclear reactions take place that power the Sun.
Temperature over 10 million °C.

Prominences
Huge clouds of gas lifted from surface by magnetic fields. Give out a lot of visible and ultraviolet radiation.
Temperature 10 to 20 thousand °C.

Chromosphere
Lower atmosphere of Sun.
Glows with pinkish light. Seen during total solar eclipse but not at other times.

Sun's diameter = 1.4 million km

Figure 1.8 A possible drawing for Activity 1.1.

Activity 1.2 Here are some typical results from this activity:

diameter of coin = 1.7 cm (5p coin)

distance of coin = 182 cm

distance ÷ diameter = 107.05882 on calculator (near enough 107).

So, for something whose angular size is that of the Moon (half a degree)

distance = 107 × diameter

diameter of Moon = 3476 km

Therefore distance of Moon = 107 × 3476 km

i.e. distance of Moon = 371 932 km (near enough 372 000 km).

To eclipse the Moon, the distance of the coin needs to be roughly a hundred times its diameter. If you tried using a coin larger than 2 cm diameter then it would need to be more than 2 m from your eye and would not fit on a 2 m rod.

Our result is quite close to the accurately measured value of 384 500 km. Yours may be closer, or not quite so close. Provided you got a value of a few hundred thousand km, then that is reasonable. If your value was very different, check back through your calculations to see if you have slipped up, and also have another look at your measurements.

Activity 2.1 At a scale of 1 cm to 10 million km the approximate distances of the planets from the Sun are: Mercury 5.8 cm; Venus 10.8 cm; Earth 15.0 cm; Mars 22.8 cm; Jupiter 77.8 cm; Saturn 143 cm (1.4 m); Uranus 2.9 m; Neptune 4.5 m; Pluto 5.9 m.

This activity illustrates one of the aspects of astronomy that most people find either fascinating or daunting — the vast scale of sizes involved. One way to get a feel for objects that seem unimaginably large and distant is to try to relate them to everyday objects — fruit, in this case.

It is a fair bet that you did not actually travel 12 km to complete this model! Even if you were unable to assemble the fruit, we hope that just reading through the activity and tables gave you a good feel for relative sizes in the Solar System.

Activity 2.2 Just about any aspect of visual appearance could be used to classify the planets and give some insight into their nature. For example, the size of a planet might well be related to the materials it is made from and the way in which it formed (and, indeed, this seems to be the case). But some aspects of visual appearance are less helpful. For instance the colours of the planets also depend on the materials that make up their surfaces, so we might expect planets of similar colour to be made of similar materials. In practice, though, colour can be misleading; Mars and Jupiter both have parts that appear red, but on Mars this is due to red-coloured rocks while Jupiter's red regions (e.g. the red spot) are due to gases in its atmosphere.

Size seems to be a useful basis of classification, with a group of small planets (Mercury, Venus, the Earth, Mars, and Pluto), and a group of large planets (Jupiter, Saturn, Uranus, and Neptune, with a possible subdivision with Jupiter and Saturn in one subclass, and Uranus and Neptune in the other).

One indication of a useful characteristic is that it ties in with others. If two different ways of classifying planets lead to the same planets being grouped together, then that suggests there may really be some underlying similarities. For example, the fact that all the planets with rings also have large numbers of natural satellites and are very much larger than Earth indicates that their similarities are not merely superficial.

Activity 2.3 The planets are believed to have formed from a rotating disc of gas and dust that surrounded the newly-formed Sun. Over about a million years, small grains of solid material gradually coagulated to form planets. Close to the Sun, the high temperatures ensured that only rocky materials formed the solid grains, hence the terrestrial planets have a largely rocky composition. Further from the Sun, where the temperatures were (and still are) much lower, icy materials were able to solidify, and so the outer planets contain large amounts of icy, as well as rocky, materials. This enabled them to reach masses large enough to capture hydrogen and helium from the solar nebula.

Activity 2.4 In the first part, you might have found that the ping-pong ball did not move exactly in a straight line. This might happen if the surface was not level, or if either the ball or table were not completely smooth. If you inadvertently spun the ball, and there was some friction between the ball and table, that too, would drive it into a curved path.

In the second part, the cork flies off in the direction it was heading, and falls in a curved path towards the Earth. It is being pulled downward by gravity. If there was no gravity it would move horizontally in a straight line.

Activity 2.5 Key points from the programme include:

- The project took 8 years from initial conception (1989) to launch (1997). The journey time to Saturn is about 7 years (1997 to 2004 in this case).

- During the development phase (in 1995) Hubble telescope data provided much more detailed information about Titan's surface, making it clear that the probe would land in a region that could be between high, dry land and a liquid-covered area.

- You saw some of the instruments being tested — for example, different designs of penetrometer were tested by dropping them on to surfaces thought to resemble that of Titan. The design was developed in the light of the test results, and you also saw the need for instruments to conform to specifications of size and weight.

Activity 2.6 Table 2.5 lists pictures in *IC* that illustrate the required processes. Your list should include a selection of these, with at least one picture in each category.

Table 2.5 Examples of processes that shape the surface of planets.

Process	Illustration(s), plate no
Craters produced by impacts	2.3, 2.4, 2.5, 2.6, 2.7, 2.8, 2.9, 2.10, 2.11, 2.15, 2.20, 2.21, 2.43, 2.44
Mountains produced by volcanoes	2.12, 2.13, 2.19, 2.24, 2.25, 2.26, 2.27, 2.28, 2.31
Regions shaped by lava flows	2.4, 2.6, 2.7, 2.9, 2.11, 2.12, 2.13, 2.17, 2.18, 2.19, 2.20, 2.21, 2.22, 2.23, 2.24, 2.26, 2.27, 2.28
Channels or canyons produced or modified by water	2.12, 2.14, 2.15

{Note that Plate 2.43 shows an asteroid, which does not really qualify as a planet or satellite.}

Activity 3.1 You should have observed that the stars in the east rise higher in the sky, and the stars in the west sink lower, and some might even set. If you made observations for several hours then the stars in the east will reach a maximum altitude and then begin to sink towards the west. This is all part of a daily cycle of stars rising in the east and setting in the west.

Activity 3.2 The answers below are for a 51.5° North planisphere.

1   The times (to the nearest 10 minutes) at which Betelgeuse is on the eastern horizon (rising) are as follows.

1 January 16.10	1 April 10.20
1 July 4.20	1 October 22.20

{Due to manufacturing variations in the planisphere, you might have obtained times up to 20 minutes earlier or later.}

2   As the lower disc is rotated anticlockwise, Betelgeuse rises until it is at its highest in the sky (in the southerly direction) at the following times

1 January 23.10	1 April 17.20
1 July 11.20	1 October 5.20

Betelgeuse continues towards the western horizon, and crosses it (sets) at

1 January 6.10	1 April 0.20
1 July 18.20	1 October 12.20

{Due to manufacturing variations in the planisphere, you might have obtained times up to 20 minutes earlier or later.}

3   The interval between the rising and setting of Betelgeuse is about 14 hours on all four dates. However, on 1 January the night is long, and Betelgeuse rises near to sunset and sets an hour or so before sunrise. It is therefore actually visible for the longest on 1 January out of the four dates.

{You might have obtained a slight difference between rising and setting from one date to another, but this is due to imprecision in the planisphere itself and in your reading of it. The interval between rising and setting of any star is the same throughout the year.}

4   The Plough does not rise or set — it is in the sky the whole time. {This depends on latitude. For example, if you were at the Equator, then the Plough *would* rise and set. Deep into the Southern Hemisphere it is always below the horizon, permanently hidden from view by the body of the Earth.}

5   Canopus never rises. {Just as the Plough is invisible from deep in the Southern Hemisphere, Canopus is invisible from high in the Northern Hemisphere. Note that the lower disc on the planisphere does not show all the stars in the sky, but only those visible at the latitude of the planisphere, plus those just out of sight.}

Activity 3.3 Your results for this activity will depend on where and when you carried it out! We hope that you will continue looking at the stars whenever you get a chance, and become familiar with their patterns and colours — particularly if you find yourself anywhere that offers clear dark skies.

If you observed several times during one night, you will have seen again (see Activity 3.1) how the stars appear to move across the sky. Like the Sun and Moon, stars rise in the east and set in the west — except for those that remain high in the sky throughout the night, which sweep around in anticlockwise circles centred on a point above the North Pole (which coincides closely with the position of the 'north star' called Polaris). The time for one complete circle about Polaris is slightly less than 24 hours (actually 23 hours 56 minutes). Any given star rises about 4 minutes earlier each day. This is hardly noticeable from one day to the next, but if you are able to extend your observations over a week or so you are more likely to be aware that stars do not return to exactly the same positions at the same time, but each night appear slightly further on in their anticlockwise motion.

If you extended your observations over a longish period (more than a few days) you might have been able to see that planets change their position relative to the stars.

Activity 4.1   See the text in Chapter 4 that follows this activity.

Activity 5.1   The key points to note from this video sequence are as follows:

- Astronomers can carry out calculations to predict how stars might form. The results of these predictions match fairly closely with observations of molecular cloud regions, which lend support to the 'story' of star formation which was used to set up the computer calculation. (If the predictions do not resemble reality, that provides a fairly strong indication that they are based on an incorrect 'story'.)

- The timescales of star formation are enormous and are measured in many millions of years. Computer simulations provide us with a 'fast forward' view which can make the process easier to visualize.

- Computer simulations and actual observations suggest that stars tend to form in pairs or larger groups rather than as isolated individuals.

Activity 5.2   After carrying out this activity you should be able to explain why we generally observe just one pulse for each revolution of a pulsar, despite the beam emerging in two directions; we could only observe two pulses if the beam emerged at right angles to the pulsar's rotation axis. The activity also illustrates how pulsars might remain unobserved — we can only see them if their radiation happens to be beamed in our direction.

Activity 5.3   Figure 5.4 shows the diagram annotated with appropriate plate numbers. Your own sketch should contain a selection of these. {Notice that the plates illustrate the stages, e.g. dense clouds, rather than processes e.g. stellar evolution.}

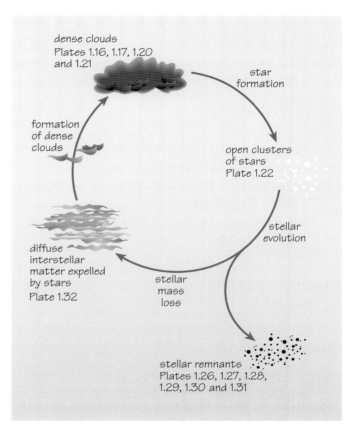

Figure 5.4   For Activity 5.3.

Activity 6.1 {Our answer consists of Table 6.1 preceded by a paragraph of overall considerations. You might have organized your answer differently. The 'Comment(s)' column in the table is not expected as part of your answer.}

The most relevant rows in the *IC* table 'Basic data on the planets' are the mean surface temperature and mean surface pressure, because these determine whether water can exist as a liquid. The row on atmospheric composition is not very relevant because it lists only the main components e.g. for the Earth, water vapour is not included because it is a minor component.

{The satellites of the planets also need to be considered. The Moon is ruled out because of its very low surface pressure and extremes of temperature, but among the satellites of the giant planets there is one promising candidate, as you will see.}

Activity 6.2 The caption to Plate 2.12 gives a clue in pointing out that some of the most heavily cratered terrain on Mars is ancient. Impact craters accumulate on a surface and are subsequently obliterated by any resurfacing (Plate 2.6). Therefore, if, on a planetary body, there is a heavily cratered terrain and a lightly cratered terrain then the heavily cratered terrain will be older. {To turn this into absolute ages we use the variously cratered terrains on the Moon, for which we have absolute ages. These have been obtained by radiometric dating of rock samples from these terrains — the details will not concern us. There are difficulties in applying lunar data to Mars, and consequently the absolute ages of the martian terrains are poorly known.}

One way of demonstrating the principle would be to prepare a smooth surface of fine sand and throw water droplets at it every few seconds. The number of pits formed by the droplets grows with every throw. The pits can be removed by resurfacing the sand. {There are many other possible demonstrations. One advantage of using water is that, as in the real case, none of each projectile (water drop) remains. In the real case they are vaporized on impact; in this demonstration they slowly evaporate.}

Table 6.1   For Activity 6.1.

Planet	Potential habitat? Reason(s)	Comment(s)
Mercury	No. Atmospheric pressure too low.	The mean surface temperature is also too low, though this is a bit misleading. Mercury rotates very slowly — it has a long day — and so one side is very hot and the other very cold.
Venus	No. Mean surface temperature much too high.	Temperatures vary little across the venusian surface, so there are no cool niches.
Mars	Unlikely. Mean surface temperature too low, and pressure is marginal.	In fact, there are places where, at certain times, the temperature can exceed 0 °C, so it is the pressure that is the problem.
Jupiter	Insufficient information given. The pressure and temperature increase with depth into the atmosphere, but it is not possible to say whether there is a level where liquid water could exist.	In fact there is an atmospheric level where the temperatures and pressures would allow liquid water, and water is present in the atmosphere. Deeper down it is too hot. But it is unlikely that life could emerge at a level in an atmosphere.
Saturn	As for Jupiter	As for Jupiter
Uranus	As for Jupiter	As for Jupiter
Neptune	As for Jupiter	As for Jupiter
Pluto	No. Too cold.	None of the surface of Pluto, at its huge distance from the Sun, gets anywhere near 0 °C. Also, the atmospheric pressure is well below 6.1 millibars.

Activity 6.3 There are no further comments to add.

Activity 7.1 Table 7.1 summarizes the distinguishing characteristics of spiral, elliptical and irregular galaxies.

Table 7.1 Characteristics used to classify galaxies.

Galaxy class	Distinguishing characteristics
Spiral	Spiral arms and central bulge. Contain regions of active star formation. (May have central bar.)
Elliptical	Elliptical outline; smooth distribution of brightness, brightest in centre. Little or no active star formation.
Irregular	No overall regular shape; uneven distribution of brightness. Contain regions of active star formation.

Activity 8.1 Suppose your unstretched band had one dot (A) 2 cm from the 'Milky Way' and another (B) at a distance of 4 cm. After stretching the band to $1\frac{1}{2}$ times its original length, the first dot would be 3 cm from the 'Milky Way' and the second 6 cm. Viewed from the 'Milky Way', dot A would have receded through 1 cm and, in the same time interval, B would have receded through 2 cm — observed from the 'Milky Way', B would have moved twice as far and twice as fast as A. This illustrates a general point: the more distant galaxies recede more rapidly than those close to the observer. This does not depend on the 'Milky Way' being in any particular location — it could be near the middle of the row of dots or at the end.

Activity 8.2 A recession speed of 5000 km per second implies a distance of 5×46 million light years i.e. 230 million light years. 10 000 km per second implies a distance of 460 million light years, and the furthest galaxies shown in Plate 3.32, with recession speeds of 15 000 km per second, have distances of 15×46 million light years i.e. 690 million light years.

One way to make the comparison is to use values from Plate 3.11 to work out the distance of an object receding at 1000 km per second. You can choose any of the objects listed. According to Plate 3.11, an object with a recession speed of 1200 km per second would lie at a distance of about 78 million light years (the galaxy labelled Virgo). To scale these values to an object receding at 1000 km per second, divide by 1.2, which gives a distance of 65 million light years.

A galaxy receding at 1000 km per second is now thought to lie at a distance of 46 million light years rather than 65 million ly. The figures given in Plate 3.11 thus show that distance measurements have been revised downwards since Plate 3.11 was produced. In other words, distant galaxies are not at quite such great distances as they were thought to be in Hubble's time — but the distances are still vast, and measured in tens or hundreds of millions of light years.

Glossary

There is a more extensive glossary near the back of *IC*. Cross-references are *italicized*.

active galaxy   A *galaxy* that produces far more *electromagnetic radiation* than can be accounted for by its *stars* and *ISM* alone.

angular size   The angle between two lines drawn from an observer's eye to opposite sides of an object.

asteroid   Small bodies found mainly between Mars and Jupiter.

atom   The smallest building block of a *molecule*.

Big Bang   The explosive event that is thought to have begun the Universe.

binary star   Two *stars* in orbit around each other.

black hole   The highly condensed remains of a *star*, whose gravity is so strong that not even light can escape.

centripetal force   A force directed towards the centre of any circular motion. Such a force is essential for maintaining motion in a curved path.

chemical compound   A substance in which the smallest unit consists of more than one type of *atom*.

chemical element   A substance containing only a single type of atom, or the atom itself.

comet   A small icy body left over from the formation of the *Solar System*, that partially evaporates if it approaches the Sun, to generate long tails.

constellation   An apparent pattern or grouping of *stars* as seen from Earth.

core (of a star)   The central very hot region where nuclear reactions can take place.

corona   The outer regions of the *Sun's* atmosphere. It is very extensive, very tenuous and very hot.

dense cloud   See *molecular cloud*.

Doppler effect   The name given to the observed change in *wavelength* in waves received from a source that is moving towards or away from an observer.

electromagnetic radiation   Collective name for gamma, X, ultraviolet, visible, infrared, microwave, and radio radiation. All these are electromagnetic waves, and are distinguished from one another by their different wavelengths.

electromagnetic spectrum   The complete range of *electromagnetic radiation*.

exoplanetary system   A system of one or more *planets* orbiting a star other than the Sun.

galaxy   A large aggregate of *stars* and *interstellar medium*, typically tens of thousands of *light years* in diameter and containing thousands of millions of *stars*.

giant planet   A *planet* considerably larger than Earth, composed largely of hydrogen and helium (cf. *terrestrial planet*).

Hubble's law   The observation that the greater a galaxy's distance, the greater the rate at which it is moving away. (The rate is proportional to the distance.)

icy materials   Materials that melt or evaporate easily, so are normally liquids or gases on the Earth's surface (cf. *rocky materials*).

interstellar medium (ISM)   The very thin gas and tiny specks of dust that lie between the *stars*.

light year   The distance that *electromagnetic radiation* travels through space in one year i.e. 9.46×10^{12} km.

lunar month   The average time between two successive new Moons, 29.53 days.

lunar phase   A particular shape of the illuminated surface of the Moon, as seen by an observer e.g. full Moon, half-moon.

main sequence star   A *star* powered by nuclear reactions of hydrogen.

meteor   A small rocky object originating outside the Earth which enters the Earth's atmosphere and is seen travelling through it.

meteorite   Any surviving fragment of a *meteor* which enters the Earth's atmosphere where it partially burns up before landing.

molecular cloud   A cold relatively dense region of the *interstellar medium*. Also known as a *dense cloud*.

molecule   The smallest unit of a substance, consisting of more than one *atom*.

nebula   A loose term, literally meaning 'cloud', applied to any interstellar object that appears extended or 'fuzzy' (in contrast to *stars*, which appear point-like).

photosphere   The bright visible 'surface' of the *Sun* or other *star*.

photosynthesis   A process in certain types of organism in which water and carbon dioxide are used in the first stage of the synthesis of complex carbon compounds, usually with the release of oxygen as a by-product.

planet   One of the nine major bodies orbiting the *Sun*, or a similar body orbiting another *star*.

planetary nebula   The glowing ejected outer layers of a *star*.

planisphere   A device for displaying which *stars* are above the horizon at any particular time on any particular date.

protostar   A collapsing fragment of a *molecular cloud* which will eventually become a *star*.

pulsar   The rapidly-spinning, dense central part of a *star* remaining after a *supernova*, detected by its regular radio pulses.

quasar   Extremely distant objects, perhaps a type of *active galaxy* that no longer exists.

red giant   A large cool *star* which is going through subsidiary stages of nuclear reactions having exhausted its hydrogen fuel supply.

redshift   The increase in *wavelength* of radiation received from a receding source (see *Doppler effect*).

rocky materials   Materials that require high temperatures in order to melt (cf. *icy materials*).

satellite   An object in orbit about a larger one, e.g. a 'moon' or an artificial space-probe orbiting a *planet*.

scientific notation   The convention of writing any number as a small number (between 1 and 10) multiplied by a power of ten e.g. 780 000 is written 7.8×10^5 and 0.000 34 is written as 3.4×10^{-4}.

solar eclipse   The partial or complete blocking of the Sun's *photosphere* by the Moon.

Solar System   Our *Sun* and all the bodies associated with it (*planets*, their *satellites*, *comets* and *asteroids*).

spectral line   A narrow line in the spectrum of *electromagnetic radiation* from a *star* or other object. The *wavelengths* of spectral lines depend on which substances are present.

star   A large near-spherical object that emits *electromagnetic radiation* by virtue of self-sustaining nuclear reactions in its interior.

Sun   The *star* at the centre of the *Solar System*.

supergiant   A *star*, several times more massive than the *Sun*, after it has exhausted its hydrogen nuclear fuel supply.

supernova   A dramatic stellar explosion, produced when a *star* several times the mass of the *Sun* has exhausted its nuclear fuel.

supernova remnant   The extended and expanding remains of a star following a *supernova*.

terrestrial planet   A *planet* similar in size to the Earth, composed of rocky material (cf. *giant planet*).

tidal heating   Heating resulting from a variation in the tidal deformation of an object (tidal deformation being the result of different gravitational forces exerted by a second object on different parts of the object in question).

wavelength   The distance from one wave peak to the next.

white dwarf   A small hot *star*, left behind when a *red giant* throws off its outer layers as a *planetary nebula*.

Acknowledgements

Grateful acknowledgement is made to the following sources for permission to reproduce material used in this course:

Figure 1.1: Robert Francis South American Pictures; *Figure 1.2*: Isla McTaggart; *Figure 1.3*: Jonathan Kern; *Figure 1.4*: Royal Astronomical Society; *Figure 1.6*: Dennis di Cicco, Sky Publishing; *Figure 2.3*: NASA; *Figure 2.4*: NASA/ESA; *Figure 2.8*: NASA/Science Photo Library; *Figure 2.9*: Akira Fujii; *Figure 4.5*: Dr Arthur Tucker/Science Photo Library; *Figure 5.2*: Copyright 1999 Lynette Cook, used with permission of the artist; Figure 6.1: Julian Baum; *Figure 6.2*: Courtesy of Derek Martin; *Figure 6.3*: NASA/JPL/MSSS; *Figure 6.4*: Prof. Colin Pillinger FRS; *Figure 6.5*: NASA/JPL; *Figure 7.1*: NASA/STScI; *Figure 7.2*: The Observatories of the Carnegie Institute of Washington; *Figure 7.3*: E. Branchini, C.S. Frenk and L. Teodoro; *Figures 7.4a and b*: The Observatories of the Carnegie Institute of Washington; *Figure 7.4c*: Dr D.W. Sciama.

Index

Entries and page numbers in bold type refer to key words which are printed in bold in the text. Section summaries, questions and activities are not indexed but answers and comments to questions and activities are. Plates in *Images of the Cosmos* are not included in this index.